OTHER SIHG PUBLICATIONS

A Guide to the Industrial History of—

Elmbridge, by Peter Tarplee, 1998
Epsom & Ewell, by Peter Wakefield, 1997
Guildford, by Francis Haveron, 1993*
Mole Valley, by Peter Tarplee, 1995
Reigate & Banstead, by Derek Stidder, 1996
Runnymede, by John Mills, 1991*
Spelthorne, by John Mills, 1993
Surrey Heath, by John Mills, 1995
Tandridge, by Malcolm Tadd, 1994
Woking, by Iain Wakeford, 1995
Waverley, in preparation

Abinger and the Royal Greenwich Observatory, by Peter Tarplee, 1996
Alexander Raby, Ironmaster: Proceedings of a Conference held at Cobham on 28 November 1998, edited by Glenys Crocker, 2000
A Guide to the Industrial Archaeology of Surrey, edited by Glenys Crocker (Association for Industrial Archaeology, 1990*)
A Guide to the Industrial Archaeology of the Waverley area, by Francis Haveron, 1985
A Guide to the Chilworth Gunpowder Mills, by Glenys Crocker, 3rd edn, 1999
Industrious Surrey: Historic Images of the County at Work, by Chris Shepheard and SIHG (Alan Sutton. 1994)
Surrey at Work in Old Photographs, by Chris Shepheard and SIHG (Alan Sutton, 1992*)
Surrey's Industrial Past, edited by Glenys Crocker, 1999
Thames Ditton Statue Foundry: the Story of the Foundry and the Preservation of its Gantry Crane, 1994

* out of print, June 2000

Damnable Inventions

Chilworth Gunpowder
and
The Paper Mills of the Tillingbourne

This pretty valley of Chilworth has a run of water which comes out of the high hills, and which, occasionally, spreads into a pond; so that there is in fact a series of ponds connected by this run of water. This valley, which seems to have been created by a bountiful providence, as one of the choicest retreats of man; which seems formed for a scene of innocence and happiness, has been, by ungrateful man, so perverted as to make it instrumental in effecting two of the most damnable of purposes; in carrying into execution two of the most damnable inventions that ever sprang from the minds of man under the influence of the devil! namely, the making of *gunpowder* and of *banknotes!*

William Cobbett, Dorking, 30 November 1822
from *Rural Rides*, 1830

Damnable Inventions

Chilworth Gunpowder
and
The Paper Mills of the
Tillingbourne

Glenys and Alan Crocker

SURREY INDUSTRIAL
HISTORY GROUP

ISBN 0 9538122 0 0

The Surrey Industrial History Group is a Group of the Surrey Archaeological Society. It aims to study, record and where appropriate preserve the remains of the former industries of the county. The Group holds meetings, lectures, visits and social events and publishes a regular *Newsletter*. Further information may be obtained from the Membership Secretary, SIHG, c/o Surrey Archaeological Society, Castle Arch, Guildford, GU1 3SX and from the Group's website: http://shs.surreycc.gov.uk/sihg/

Cover illustrations
Main: Gunpowder workers at Chilworth *c.*1913. Courtesy of Ron Puddick.
Lower front: Engraving of Albury Park paper mill in about 1800 (actual size). Courtesy of Guildford Museum.
Lower back: Making paper by hand, from *The Penny Magazine*, 1833.

Printed by J W Arrowsmith Ltd, Bristol

Contents

List of illustrations

Cover illustrations
Gunpowder workers at Chilworth *c*.1913
Engraving of Albury Park paper mill, *c*.1800
Making paper by hand, 1833

Illustrations in the Text

Preface and Acknowledgements

This book is a combined and expanded new edition of *Chilworth Gunpowder* by Glenys Crocker, published by the Surrey Industrial History Group in 1984, and *The Paper Mills of the Tillingbourne* by Alan Crocker, privately published in a limited edition by the Tabard Press in 1988. The two industries are brought together under the title 'Damnable Inventions' after William Cobbett, who deplored the use of the waters of the Tillingbourne for the manufacture of gunpowder and banknote paper.

Research on the Chilworth powder mills has made considerable progress since 1984, largely through the contacts and influence of the Gunpowder Mills Study Group which the present authors and Phil Philo, then of Gunnersbury Park Museum, started in 1986. Our debt to individual members of the GMSG is impossible to record but we are grateful to them all for sharing their knowledge. Three in particular require mention. Besides our own continuing work, a major contribution has been made by Keith Fairclough on the powder mills in the seventeenth century and the first half of the eighteenth. His papers on Sir Polycarpus Wharton and on the involvement of the philanthropist Thomas Coram in the gunpowder business were published in 1996 and 1999 respectively. At the time of writing his work on the East India Company, the Cordwells and Huguenot powdermakers is nearing publication and we are grateful to him for permission to use it in the present book. We would like to thank Wayne Cocroft for access to the text of his book *Dangerous Energy*, also shortly to be published as the present book goes to press. Thanks are also due to the Group's members at the ETBA

Cultural Foundation in Athens for providing the photograph of stamp mills at Dimitsana.

A great deal of progress has also been made in our understanding of the history of papermaking in this area. Publication of *The Paper Mills of the Tillingbourne* in 1988 coincided with the 500th anniversary of the establishment of the first paper mill in England, which was at Hertford. This was commemorated by a conference of the International Association of Paper Historians partly in Durham and partly at Hertford. We attended this meeting and were active in founding the British Association of Paper Historians in 1989. Members of BAPH, particularly Robin Clarke and Peter Bower, have helped us to discover much additional information. Also, publication of the book resulted in our meeting Anne Phillips, a descendant of the Ball family who were papermakers in the Tillingbourne valley from 1790 to 1824. As a family historian she has provided us with a wealth of valuable information. We have also been fortunate in finding new material in the Northamptonshire Record Office, in the archive deposited by the Spencer family who inherited the Chilworth estate from the Duchess of Marlborough.

We are indebted to the staff of the many libraries and record offices whose services we have used; to local people at Chilworth, Albury and Blackheath, particularly our colleagues in the Chilworth Gunpowder Mills Working Group, for their interest and enthusiasm for the project; to our colleagues in the Surrey Industrial History Group; and to all those who have participated in our tours of the sites, for the information and interpretations they have provided and the challenging questions they have posed. We are especially grateful to those who have provided illustrations for this volume.

Alan and Glenys Crocker
Guildford, March 2000

A note on sources of information

References to sources are given at the end of each chapter. In the case of manuscript sources the relevant library or record office is given. We have also been given access to much material in private hands and in due course we propose to deposit the resulting transcripts, notes and copies with the Surrey Archaeological Society (SyAS). Enquiries can be made through the Society at Castle Arch, Guildford GU1 3SX.

Abbreviations

Aubrey: Aubrey, J, *Natural History and Antiquities of the County of Surrey*, 1718–19, 5 vols (rep. Dorking, 1975)

BAPH: British Association of Paper Historians

Gazetteer: *Gunpowder Mills Gazetteer: Black Powder Manufacturing Sites in the British Isles*, compiled by G Crocker for GMSG (SPAB, Wind & Watermill Section, 1988)

General Survey 1728: General Survey of Chillworth St Martha, British Library Manuscripts, Althorp Papers, PG4, General

GMSG: Gunpowder Mills Study Group

Gunpowder Mills: Documents: Crocker, A G, Crocker, G M, Fairclough, K R & Wilks, M J, *Gunpowder Mills: Documents of the Seventeenth and Eighteenth Centuries*, Surrey Record Society vol.36, forthcoming 2000

IPH: International Association of Paper Historians

Manning & Bray: Manning, O & Bray, W, *The History and Antiquities of the County of Surrey*, 1804–14, 3 vols (rep. Wakefield, 1974)

NEO: Northumberland Estates Offices at Albury and Alnwick

NRO, SOX 488: Northamptonshire Record Office, Spencer Papers

PRO: Public Record Office

SHC: Surrey History Centre, Woking

Shorter, *Paper Making*: Shorter, A H, *Paper Making in the British Isles* (Newton Abbot, 1971)

Shorter, *Paper Mills*: Shorter, A H, *Paper Mills and Paper Makers in England, 1495–1800* (Hilversum, 1957)

Simmons Collection: Simmons, H E S, The Simmons Water Mills Collec-
   tion: unpublished manuscript notes, 1940s, held by the Science Museum
   Library, London. Copy of Surrey section also in SyAS Library
SPAB: Society for the Protection of Ancient Buildings
StRO: Staffordshire Record Office
SyAC: Surrey Archaeological Collections
SyAS: Surrey Archaeological Society
VCH: The Victoria History of the County of Surrey, 1902–12, 4 vols.

1

The Tillingbourne Valley

The Surrey stream known as the Tillingbourne rises near the sand-stone summit of Leith Hill, which at 294 metres is the highest point in south-east England. For the first 4 kilometres of its course it flows northwards over a series of picturesque weirs and cascades towards the North Downs, the chalk escarpment which forms the southern boundary of the Thames Basin and the northern edge of the Weald. At the 120 metre contour, near Wotton House, it turns westwards and falls steadily for a further 14 kilometres until it joins the River Wey at Shalford, which is only 30 metres above sea level. The Wey then flows northwards through the gap in the North Downs at Guildford and continues for a further 25 kilometres to its confluence with the River Thames at Weybridge.

The Tillingbourne, as shown in the detail of Senex's 1729 map of Surrey reproduced as figure 1, passes through the attractive villages of Abinger Hammer, marked 'Shire Hammer', Gomshall, Shere, Albury, Weston Street and Chilworth, also known as St Martha's, before reaching Shalford. It has four principal tributaries. First the stream from the mill pond at Friday Street, a popular beauty spot to the south, joins it at Wotton House, the home of members of the Evelyn family who were active in industry and estate management. Then there is the stream which rises below the Iron Age hillfort at Holmbury St Mary, and flows northwards to join the Tillingbourne at Abinger Hammer. This was one of the forges of the Wealden iron industry, established before 1557 and active until about 1787.[1] Next, flowing into the Tillingbourne from the north at Albury, comes the Sherbourne Brook, which is fed by the chalk springs of Silent Pool. This name was invented by the versifier Martin Tupper,

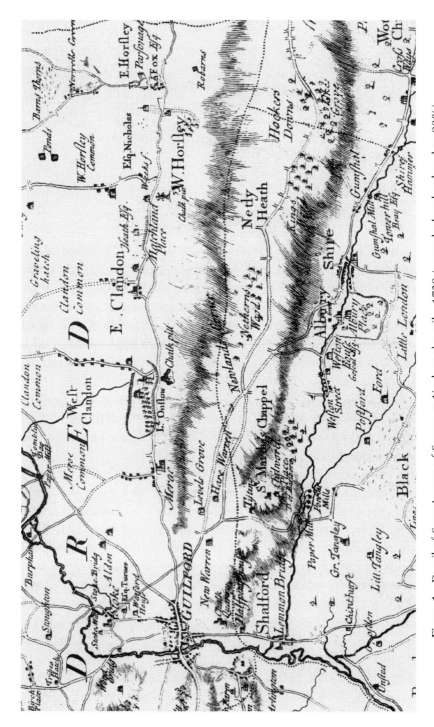

Figure 1 Detail of Senex's map of Surrey at 1inch to the mile, 1729 (retouched and reduced to 90%). Courtesy of Surrey Archaeological Society.

who lived at Albury in Weston House, which is marked on the map in figure 1. He was famous in the early Victorian period for his moralising *Proverbial Philosophy*, which went through some fifty editions. In his novel *Stephan Langton, a Romance of the Silent Pool*, he created the legend of how King John surprised a local girl bathing in the pond and caused her to drown.[2] Finally the Postford or Law Brook joins the Tillingbourne from the south near the Chilworth gunpowder mills. It here forms the boundary between the parishes of Albury and St Martha and is clearly but not very accurately drawn in figure 1.

The parish church of St Martha stands to the north on top of a sandstone hill 140 metres above the Tillingbourne. An east–west trackway, popularly known as 'The Pilgrims' Way', leads to the church. This name was introduced in the 1860s by a romantic Ordnance Survey officer and its use on maps tends to give it a false authenticity. There is however no evidence that the path forms part of a route used by pilgrims travelling to Canterbury.[3] The church is the only one in England dedicated to St Martha. There is a legend that, after the Ascension, Martha left the Holy Land and settled in Provence where a dragon lived on the banks of the Rhone, terrifying the local people. Martha's faith was strong enough to enable her to capture the dragon which was then killed. An alternative and happier conclusion to the tale is that Martha so influenced the beast with her courage that it became a good dragon and subsequently helped in her works of mercy.[4]

The combined waters of the Tillingbourne and its tributaries produce only a small river, even at its confluence with the Wey, but its steep gradient and constant flow make it ideal for driving waterwheels. Many corn mills and early industrial sites were therefore located along its course.[5]

In 1676 John Evelyn, the diarist and author of *Sylva*, the first book in English on forestry, wrote a letter to John Aubrey which was printed as a foreword to Aubrey's *History of Surrey*, edited by Richard Rawlinson and published posthumously in 1718–19. Referring to the neighbourhood of his brother George's house at Wotton, Evelyn stated: 'I do not remember to have seen such Variety of Mills and Works upon so narrow a Brook, and in so little a Compass; there being Mills for Corn, Cloth, Brass, Iron, Powder etc.'[6] As yet there were no paper mills on the Tillingbourne, although several had been established nearby, but the valley had become a major centre of gunpowder manufacture, had held a Crown monopoly before the Civil War and become the largest manufacturing site in the country since that conflict.

Notes

1. Cleere, H F & Crossley, D W, *The Iron Industry of the Weald* (2nd edn 1995), 309.
2. Alexander, M, *Tales of Old Surrey* (1985), 61–3.
3. *Tales of Old Surrey*, 20–2.
4. Taylor, J W, *The Coming of the Saints* (1906).
5. Brandon, P, 'Land, Technology and Water Management in the Tillingbourne Valley, Surrey', *Southern History*, vol.6 (1984), 75–103.
6. Aubrey, vol.1, following p.xlviii.

2

The Early Gunpowder Industry

In his letter to Aubrey, John Evelyn claimed that his ancestors brought the invention of gunpowder manufacture to England and Aubrey himself stated that the Chilworth powder mills were the first in England,[1] a claim that was repeated on Bowen's Map of Surrey of 1753. Following this tradition, the Chilworth Gunpowder Company in the late nineteenth century printed 'Established 1570' on its publicity material. In fact, the Chilworth powder mills were not established until 1626 and the earliest recorded water-driven powder mills in England were at Rotherhithe in the 1540s. Before that, gunpowder was made by hand, by mixing and crushing together the ingredients — saltpetre (potassium nitrate), charcoal and sulphur (formerly known as brimstone) — with a pestle and mortar. Most of the powder used in England was imported or made from imported ingredients.

The old measure of gunpowder was the 'last' of 24cwt. In the late sixteenth century the government specified that each last was to contain 18cwt of double-refined saltpetre, 3cwt of brimstone of Naples and 3cwt of charcoal, giving proportions of $75:12\frac{1}{2}:12\frac{1}{2}$.[2] Only the charcoal was easily obtainable as it was made in pitsteads in the woods in the traditional way, as shown in figure 2. Sulphur had to be imported from volcanic regions and the main ingredient, saltpetre, from places with a hot climate and a pronounced dry season, such as North Africa and India, where it forms readily. Saltpetre was also found in colder climates as an efflorescence on the walls of buildings which contained nitrogenous organic material, such as stables. The conditions for its formation could be created

Figure 2 Three stages in the traditional method of charcoal burning in clamps, from John Evelyn's *Sylva* (1664). Courtesy of the Surrey Archaeological Society.

artificially so that larger quantities could be obtained from collected manure but the process was not well understood in England.

Both gunpowder and raw materials came in mainly through Antwerp, which was in the Spanish Netherlands, and as relations with Spain worsened during the reign of Elizabeth I it became necessary to secure better supplies at home. In 1560 it was recommended that 'the Quene's Majestie should do well to macke out of hande, four or six mylles for the macking of powdyr for the servize of her Highness' turne, if the warres contynew, or this breach of amytie should channce betwixt her Majestie and King Philipe'. In the following year instructions 'for making saltpetre to growe' were purchased from a German captain, Gerard Honrick. The process involved a heap of black earth collected from such places as dovecotes and stables to which urine, dung and lime were added. It was turned at intervals over several months until salts had formed which were extracted in solution. The liquor was then boiled down and cooled so that crystals of saltpetre were precipitated.

Gunpowder mills set up by the Evelyn family on the Hogsmill river at Tolworth in Surrey may date from the period of these developments, since it is known that George Evelyn acquired the manor of Tolworth in 1561.[3] In 1579 the Evelyns purchased the Wotton

Figure 3 Pigeon houses were a major source of saltpetre earth. There was a highly-organised regional system of collection in the seventeenth century. This example of an interior, showing the potence which gave access to the nesting boxes, is at Avoncroft open-air museum, Bromsgrove, Worcestershire. Photo by Glenys Crocker.

estate in the Tillingbourne valley and ten years later an estate at Godstone in south-east Surrey.

After the defeat of the Spanish Armada the government realised that the supply of gunpowder was still inadequate and began to appoint manufacturers by Royal letters patent. In 1589 a contract was made with George Evelyn, his son John and Richard Hill to obtain saltpetre and manufacture gunpowder. They set up mills on the Tillingbourne at Wotton and Abinger, which they converted to copper mills in the 1620s, and at Godstone, where they continued to manufacture gunpowder until the 1630s.

In 1621 James I appointed the Lords of the Admiralty as Commissioners for Saltpetre and Gunpowder. The country was divided into districts for collection and saltpetre men were appointed who were given weekly quotas to fulfil and had the right to enter premises to dig for nitrogenous earth. The state papers of the period contain numerous letters of complaint about their activities. Although inhabited dwellings were exempt, this rule was sometimes disregarded. Dovecotes, such as the one shown in figure 3, were a favoured source of material and many had their walls undermined by digging.

A series of three-year contracts was awarded to the Evelyn family for gunpowder, for 120 lasts (144 tons) in 1621 and for double this amount in 1624. Two-thirds of the gunpowder made was to be delivered to the government's stores in the Tower of London and the rest could be sold to merchant seamen and other private subjects.[4]

The system of Crown appointments which had begun under Elizabeth I became a monopoly in which a sole powdermaker to the king was appointed and efforts were made to suppress other manufacturers. It was against this background that special permission was granted to the East India Company to manufacture gunpowder for its own use and that the powder mills at Chilworth were established in 1626.

Notes

This chapter is based mainly on the section on gunpowder in the *Victoria County History of Surrey (VCH)*, vol.2, 306–29. For a short account of the history and technology of the industry, see Crocker, G, *The Gunpowder Industry* (2nd edn 1999). For details of individual manufacturing sites see *Gunpowder Mills Gazetteer* (SPAB, Wind & Watermill Section, 1988).

1. Aubrey, vol. 1, following p. xlviii, vol. 4, 57.
2. *VCH*, vol.2, 315–6.
3. Crocker, G & A, 'Gunpowder mills of Surrey', *Surrey History*, vol.4 no.3 (1990), 134–158, at p.139.
4. *VCH*, vol.2, 316.

3

The East India Company, the King's Mills and the Civil War

The East India Company was involved at Chilworth for only ten years and then the mills were expanded to supply the government of Charles I. The Company made gunpowder for Parliament during the Civil War.

The East India Company

The Company of Merchants of London Trading into the East Indies, better known as the East India Company, had received its charter in 1600. First the Portuguese and then the Dutch had already established a lucrative spice trade with the Far East so there was serious rivalry and the Company's ships were heavily armed. When the government was preparing for war with Spain in the 1620s, the East India Company was finding it difficult to obtain sufficient gunpowder for its ships' defence and, after much deliberation, decided that the best plan was to manufacture its own.[1]

Because the gunpowder industry was run as a Crown monopoly the Company had to obtain a licence to set up and operate its own mills. This was granted in 1625, solely for the manufacture of gunpowder for the Company's own use, and a water corn mill was acquired and converted for the purpose. Its site, described as being 'in the skirts of Windsor Forest', has been identified as that of Trumps Mill at Thorpe, on the Bourne near Egham.

The government's powdermakers used saltpetre made from compost collected by the saltpetre men but the East India Company had access to the rich resources in India and began to import saltpetre for use in its own mills. Later in the seventeenth century imported saltpetre replaced the domestic product throughout the industry.

Having obtained a licence and a manufacturing site, the East India Company appointed William Blyth, who had been saltpetre man for the north-west of England, as powdermaker to supervise setting up the mills and Edward Collins of its London office as clerk. Collins had earlier served the Company in the Far East and was a survivor of the notorious Amboyna Massacre of February 1623. Dutch traders in the Spice Islands had accused a group of English factors of plotting to seize their trading station on Amboyna, had imprisoned and tortured them and had executed most of the group. Collins's life had been spared 'by the drawing of lots' and he had returned to London, his health, and doubtless his nerves, the worse for his experience. Appointing him to a position at a gunpowder works was apparently seen as a suitable way of providing him with some security.

The mills at Thorpe had scarcely been established when they were ordered to be closed because they interfered with the feeding of the deer in Windsor Forest. An alternative site had to be found, and Chilworth was chosen. It is not known how this came about but it may be significant that the Governor of the East India Company was Sir Morris (Maurice) Abbot, who was born in Guildford and whose brothers George and William were Archbishop of Canterbury and Bishop of Winchester respectively. Morris Abbot probably had local knowledge of a disused corn mill and fulling mill in the manor of Chilworth, at the dam where the modern Blacksmith Lane crosses the Tillingbourne.

The manor had belonged to Sir John Morgan who had died in 1621. It was now owned jointly by his daughter Anne and her husband Sir Edward Randyll, and by his widow Elizabeth Morgan and her husband John Sotherton.What ensued is known from records of a case against the Company which was brought to the Court of Exchequer by the landowners in 1631.[2] Depositions were taken in evidence from local people, one of whom, a wheelwright named Thomas Poole of Albury, had been tenant of the old fulling mill when William Blyth first came to view the site. His statement was recorded as follows:

William Blith . . . did first treat with this deponent concerning the taking or assignment of his lease about half a year before his entry. And told this deponent that he would use the said fulling mill for grinding of wheate but he did not acquaynte this deponent for whom he would take the same.

   The damm head of the said mill ponnd in the grates and groundworks of the said wast water gates and the mayne sewer and sluice were in decay which this deponent did then shewe to the said Mr Blith and told him that the same must be spedily repaired least the water in the said pond should break down the said pond head, who made light thereof and told this deponent, binding it with a great oath, that he cared not if he went to Lawe with the Devill for they that sett him at work had money enough.

The Company moved on to the site in September 1626, converted the disused buildings to gunpowder mills and raised the level of the dam to gain more power. This caused water to back up the valley and flood the landlords' hop gardens. Then in May 1627 the dam gave way. Workmen at the powder mills opened the main sluice to empty the pond, to prevent worse damage, and the landlords' carp were washed out into the meadows below the dam, where they were gleefully collected up by the people of East Shalford.

Besides problems with the mill pond, there was an explosion at the mills in 1628. Accidents were fairly common at powder mills, but most, like this one, were not serious. A worse explosion occurred in 1630 which resulted in the mills being rebuilt. Their locations are significant for tracing the development of industry on the site.

The sequence of sketch maps in figure 4 shows how the watercourses and mill sites probably appeared at successive dates in the seventeenth century. The first accurate survey of the manor was made in 1728[3] and a detail of this is reproduced in chapter 7. Since watermills tended to continue in the same place for many years, this survey has been used as a basis for the sketch maps.

The disused corn mill was probably on the site of the mill recorded at *Celeorde* in the Domesday survey of 1086. It is assumed here that it was near the middle of the dam and that the dam retained a conventional triangular mill pond. The fulling mill was first recorded in 1589[4] but had probably been established in the Middle Ages when the woollen industry flourished in the district and water-powered fulling stocks were used for the controlled shrinking and thickening of woven cloth. One of the East India Company's powder mills was erected on the site of the corn mill and two were close together on the sites of the fulling mill and its adjacent dwelling house. It is

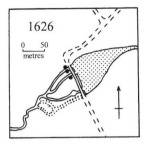

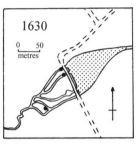

Figure 4 Chilworth powder mills: suggested stages of expansion, 1626–54. Black dots: mills; dashed lines: roads and trackways; dotted lines: probable leat of disused wire mill.

1626: Three powder mills at Chilworth mill pond, at the modern Blacksmith Lane.

1630: Explosion. Two mills rebuilt, the third replaced by a mill on the wireworks leat.

1636: The king's mills built at Postford (Upper Works) and expanded at Chilworth (Lower Works). Chilworth mill pond reconstructed with two dams and a culvert.

1652–4: First Dutch War. Middle Works built on a new cut taken off the Tillingbourne below Postford Pond.

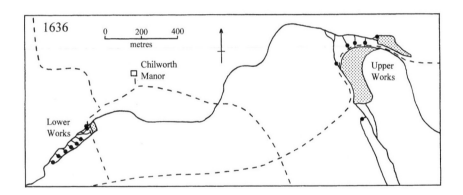

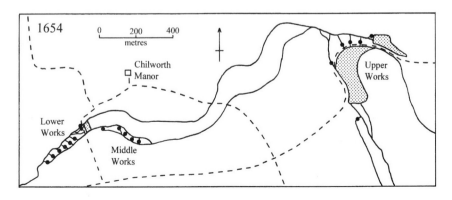

assumed that these were to the north of the corn mill, where two waterwheel symbols are shown on the 1728 survey.

It came to be appreciated that gunpowder mills should not be built too close together, in case an explosion in one spreads to the others. After the 1630 accident the mill on the site of the fulling mill house was replaced by one at a safer distance, downstream of the dam. This area was known as Steersland, probably after Thomas Steere who had set up wire mills at Chilworth in 1603.[5] He was infringing a monopoly held by the Mineral and Battery Works, whose main operations were at Tintern in Monmouthshire (modern Gwent) and had been forced to close and dismantle the works in 1606. The site had probably remained vacant since then but the leat, shown by dotted lines on the 1626 sketch map in figure 4, would have remained ready to be re-instated.

Despite the practical problems of safety and managing the water courses, the Company's powder-making venture had some success. Enough powder was produced for some to be sold to private customers and at first the authorities turned a blind eye. Nevertheless the Company wished to reduce costs and in 1628 decided to sub-contract its plant to a manufacturer rather than manage the operation itself. In December 1628 a contract was awarded to Edward Collins, who by then had been instructed in the technical side of the business by William Blyth. The Company continued to hold the head lease of the mills and the letters patent authorising the manufacture.

Collins was unable to make a success of the business. In March 1629 there began the period of the king's personal rule, when Charles I dissolved parliament and determined to rule without it. Deprived of the taxes it normally granted, he had to find other sources of income and began to operate the gunpowder monopoly to this end. The East India Company's sales to private customers were no longer tolerated and in 1632 its letters patent were withdrawn. The mills lay idle, Collins fell into debt, his workmen into poverty and the mill pond into disrepair. Some relief came in 1634 when the Company was permitted to 'repair' old gunpowder which had deteriorated in storage or at sea. Edward Collins had gone to New England, for reasons unknown, and his wife Sarah was given the contract and had two of the mills brought back into production.

The East India Company's disputes with the Randylls, which had gone to the Court of Exchequer in 1631, involved not only the Company's management of the site but the validity of their lease, which had not been properly signed by all parties in 1626. The Company tried to placate their landlords with offers of spices and a velvet gown, but to no avail. There was also a quarrel within the Randyll family about the fulfilment of the heir's marriage settlement: Sir Morgan, Sir Edward Randyll's eldest son, had been persuaded by pecuniary expectations to marry his lady, Anne, when he 'preferred another' and the dispute became so acrimonious that in 1633 he threatened to pull down the mills.[6] In 1635 therefore, when an anonymous 'gentleman of quality' came to enquire whether the Company was prepared to sell or lease the mills, it was happy to comply.

The enquiry may have come from someone preparing to bid for the government contract, or from the government itself, for the king was planning to take control of the industry and run it for his own profit. He was negotiating with the Evelyns about the price of gunpowder, which was currently supplied to him at 8d per pound. They were unwilling to reduce their price so alternative suppliers were being sought.

Edward Collins, now back from New England, was ordered to put the Chilworth mills in working order and make a trial production run. This proved highly successful and in the autumn of 1635 Collins was given a government contract to supply 200 barrels of gunpowder per month. This contract was renewed only up to autumn 1636 and the Chilworth powdermakers were then awarded the gunpowder monopoly in Evelyn's place. The new arrangements meant a large increase in the amount of gunpowder produced nationally so the East India Company was given a contract to supply imported saltpetre.

Edward Collins died during the course of the negotiations over government contracts and the new partnership which undertook the 1636 contract was that of Samuel Cordwell of Higham in Kent and George Collins.

Cordwell & Collins and the King's Mills

Samuel Cordwell was new to Chilworth and to the gunpowder industry. He had obtained wealth and contacts through service in the king's household and was brought in to provide financial backing and to organise and control the business. Although he lived in Kent and at his London home in Lambeth, he acquired property at

Abinger in the Tillingbourne valley and made several bequests to the poor of that village.[7] He was evidently the dominant partner in the gunpowder business. He obtained the lease to the mills and purchased equipment and raw materials from Sarah Collins, Edward's widow, and he was referred to as the 'king's powdermaker'.

George Collins's exact relationship to his predecessor Edward is not clear but he was probably a member of the same family and had learned the art of powdermaking from Edward, who in turn had learned it from William Blyth. He brought technical expertise to the partnership and lived in the locality.

It appears that in 1636 Samuel Cordwell was acting as an agent of the king at Chilworth and the king provided a loan of £2000 for the expansion of the manufacturing plant. In 1641 Cordwell suggested that he be excused repayment of this loan so that the mills would become the property of the king when the lease expired in 1649. Charles considered this seriously and even considered purchasing the land from the Randyll family, but political developments leading up to the Civil War intervened. In 1649 the king was executed and his loan never was repaid. After the restoration of the monarchy in 1660 the lord of the manor, Vincent Randyll, was unsure of his right of ownership and petitioned Charles II to confirm it. There is no record of such confirmation being given but there is no evidence either that the king ever laid claim to the mills.[8]

The Chilworth powder mills expanded over the next decades so that by 1677 a survey, in writing, carried out for the Ordnance by Sir Jonas Moore stated that 'these Mills are divided into three several works by the distance that the course of water makes to gett a fall for each work. Vizt. the Lower, Midle, and Upper works'. It goes on to explain that 'the Lower work was the first work of the three' and that 'the Midle work was built by Mr Randill in the first Dutch warr' (which was in 1652–4), but it says nothing about the origin of the Upper Works, only that it was 'once a Compleat Work of it selfe'.[9] No other explicit evidence has been found.

A rough estimate of how many mills there were at different times can be made from the known output of the works — the quantity of gunpowder for which contracts were awarded.

There is a confusion over the use of the word 'mill,' which can mean either an entire works or merely one individual process unit. At the time, a 'mill' seems to have meant the unit for incorporating gunpowder which was powered by one waterwheel. There were mills for other processes in gunpowder production but for these the word 'mill' is always qualified, as in 'brimstone mill'.

In 1677 there were seven incorporating mills at the Lower Works, two at the mill pond and five along the leat on Steersland. In addition there were six at the Upper Works. Not all would have produced the same amount of motive power but they would be roughly comparable. The East India Company could make 30 barrels of gunpowder per week with three mills. The 1635 contract was for 50 per week, which suggests five mills, and these could have been accommodated at the Lower Works. The 1636 contract however was for 120 barrels per week, so the Upper Works would also have been needed.

There is in fact a tantalisingly brief, inexplicit, mis-spelled and half-dated record that a meeting was to be held at Hampton Court, on Friday 18 November, to discuss the concerns of several local people who lived at 'Ailesbury' and Chilworth. These were Mr Duncombe, an attorney of the King's Bench, Mr Bushby, Henry Wardner, John Matthewes, Rob Bruburne, Richard Collier and Joseph Tickner.[10] 'Ailesbury' was clearly Albury, for the Upper Works lay partly in that parish, and several of the names are those of local people. The Duncombes were a prominent family in the district, Mr Bushby is probably a mis-spelling of Boothby, who with Richard Collier is known from Albury manor records. Friday 18 November could only have been in 1636, and the note implies that the mills had already been built.

The Upper and Lower Works in 1636 were therefore much as they were described in 1677, and roughly as they are shown on Seller's map of Surrey of c.1679 (figure 5). Seller's map also marks the Middle Works, which was built in the 1650s, but does not actually depict its features. The streams and waterwheel symbols shown are all those of the Lower and Upper Works. They are inaccurate in detail and distances are distorted, but this, on a small-scale map of the whole county, is perhaps not surprising. The lay-out of the works as they might actually have appeared in 1636 is shown in the sequence of sketch maps in figure 4.

The building of the Upper Works involved the construction of massive earthworks, which can still be seen today at Postford. The great curved dam of Postford Pond, where there were four mills, retains both the Tillingbourne and its tributary the Postford Brook,

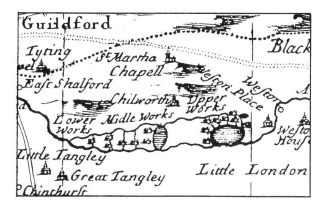

Figure 5 Detail of John Seller's map of Surrey, *c.*1679. Although the Middle Works is named, the features represented appear to be those of the Lower and Upper Works only.

and separates them from Waterloo Pond (Pens or Paynes Pond before the battle of 1815), which is fed by springs. Another dam was built at the lower end of Pens Pond, where there was one mill, and a leat about a kilometre long was taken off the Postford Brook to serve a mill just above where the Brook enters Postford Pond.

Major earth-moving was also needed at the Lower Works, both to build further mills on Steersland, downstream of the dam of Chilworth mill pond, and to repair the damage and make good the watercourses which had been such a bone of contention during the East India Company's tenancy. This resulted in the mill pond acquiring the unusual form which it still has today, as shown in the maps for 1636 and 1654 in figure 4 and in figures 6 and 7. It has two dams, a conventional one at the downstream end and another at the upstream end. This was clearly the solution to the problem of flooding the hop grounds. However, the valley floor still had to be drained or a second pond would have formed behind the upper dam. A culvert was therefore made under both the mill pond and the dam to drain the valley floor and this is still used to control the level of water in a large fishing pond which was made in the 1980s. Its inlet can be seen when the water is taken down periodically, as shown in figure 8. The pond having been dammed at both ends, the Tillingbourne had to be diverted into it, so an embanked channel was constructed to enter the pond on the north side. There is a possibility that this channel was an ancient mill-stream, used before a pond was made for the early mill, and that it was only re-instated in 1636.[11]

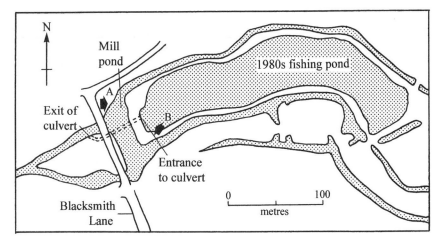

Figure 6 Sketch map of the Chilworth ponds, 1980s, showing the old mill pond entered by two streams, the culvert underneath it and the modern fishing pond. The bold arrows show the directions in which the photographs in figure 7 (point A) and figure 8 (point B) were taken.

Figure 7 Chilworth ponds, looking east from Blacksmith Lane. The old mill pond is in the foreground. At its far end is the second dam which was built in the 1630s to stop the water backing up the valley. Beyond is the large modern fishing pond, seen when the water had been taken down in February 1998. Photo by Glenys Crocker.

Figure 8 Entrance to the culvert (below the railing) which was made under the old Chilworth mill pond to drain the valley floor, looking north-west. The culvert is used to control the level of water in the modern fishing pond, which is shown with the water taken down in February 1998. Photo by Glenys Crocker.

Whether the works at Chilworth mill pond were financed by the king or by the landowners, the Randylls, is not known, but the king's £2000 was stated to be for 'the building of Mills, Worke howses, Stoaves, Stoare howses, and the providinge of Utensils'. It may be observed that what appear to be dauntingly ambitious works of construction seem to have been undertaken quite readily, and remarkably quickly, in the past, probably because plenty of labour was available at slack times in the farming year.

So the 'king's mills' were set up. Surrey JPs were instructed to see that local people's obligation to provide transport — the king's right of purveyance — was fulfilled. Powder and materials had to be carried by land from Chilworth to Ham Haw wharf at the mouth of the Wey, for the river was not yet made navigable. The saltpetre men were instructed to deliver their product to Cordwell's new warehouse in Southwark. Merchants who imported brimstone were instructed to ensure that enough was left unrefined for the powdermakers, as sulphur for gunpowder needed special treatment. And Cordwell and Collins began to carry out their contract successfully.

Late in 1640 however they stopped making deliveries to the Ordnance. The high prices which the king was charging private customers for gunpowder were greatly resented and illicit production and sales were going on. The monopoly broke down even before the Long Parliament, which the king was forced to call in 1640, formally ended it in August 1641. In November the king was presented with a long list of grievances known as the Grand Remonstrance. This included complaints about the way the gunpowder monopoly had been operated and also about the activities of the saltpetre men, who had the right to enter people's properties and dig up their floors. The king rejected the whole catalogue of complaints, the political situation continued to deteriorate, and in August 1642 the Civil War broke out.

The Civil War

Although the monopoly was cancelled in 1641 it was not until the war started that powder mills were established elsewhere (except for illegal ones which had been operating at Bristol and elsewhere). Then in 1642 John Berisford began producing gunpowder for the parliamentary side at Sewardstone and Temple Mills on the River Lea in Essex. These mills were untroubled by the conflict but Chilworth was caught up in it and in 1642 the mills were slighted by both sides, first by Parliament and then by the king, because, as his warrant for their destruction explained:

> Whereas Wee understand that the Powder Milnes at Chilworth in the County of Surrey, have been lately made unserviceable, to the end that Wee might not make use of them, and yet are left in such condicon, as they may bee easily repaired when Wee are gone out of this Countrey.

The mills were back in use by March 1643 and continued to supply the parliamentary side during the war. The royalists set up mills around the country as needed, in particular at Oxford and Bristol, and both sides used imported gunpowder, especially from the Netherlands.[12]

There was another royalist raid on Chilworth in July 1643 but the mills were not damaged again during the war. Safety precautions had to be taken — the Committee for the Militia of London appointed 'a careful Man' to accompany deliveries of saltpetre to the works and Cordwell was ordered to deliver all gunpowder to the Tower immediately and never to keep more than one week's supply of saltpetre at Chilworth.

George Collins died in 1644 and Samuel Cordwell in 1648. Samuel was succeeded by his brother Robert, who continued to supply the Ordnance until his death in 1650. Robert's widow Mrs Mary Cordwell continued the business for a few months but found it beyond her abilities and sold her stock to some merchants who became tenants of the lord of the manor.

Notes

1. Fairclough, K R, 'The East India Company and Gunpowder Production in England, 1625–1636', *SyAC*, vol.87 (2000).
2. PRO, Exchequer Depositions by Commission: E134/ 7 Chas I, 5 Mich.
3. BL, MSS, General Survey of Chillworth St Martha, 1728 (Althorp Papers, PG4, General)
4. Manning & Bray, vol.2, 117–118.
5. Crocker, G, 'Seventeenth Century Wireworks in Surrey and the Case of Thomas Steere', *Surrey History*, vol.6 no.1 (1999), 2–16.
6. Fairclough, 'East India Company' (see note 1), Appendix: The Ownership of Chilworth Mills.
7. Information provided by Keith Fairclough.
8. Fairclough, K R, 'The Cordwell Family: Gunpowder Producers at Chilworth, 1636–1650', *SyAC*, vol.87 (2000).
9. StRO, Dartmouth Papers, D742/M/ 1/13. The lieutenant-general of the Ordnance in the 1670s was Col. William Legge, of the family which became earls of Dartmouth.
10. Fairclough, see note 8.
11. Crocker, G, 'Mill Sites and Watercourses in the Manor of Chilworth: Research in Progress', *SyAS Bulletin*, 328 (April 1999), 5–8.
12. Edwards, P, 'Gunpowder and the English Civil War', *J Arms & Armour Society*, vol.15 (1995), 109–31.

4

Josias Dewye, Vincent Randyll and Sir Polycarpus Wharton

Sir Edward Randyll had died in 1646 and Chilworth Manor had passed to Vincent Randyll, his second son. His eldest son, Sir Morgan, with whom he had been quarrelling in 1633, had been declared insane in 1640 at the request of his hapless wife and had died four years later. Vincent Randyll was later to take up gunpowder manufacture himself.

First however the mills were occupied by an expert powdermaker named Josias Dewye, who had taken a lease of powdermills in the Lea valley in 1650 before moving to Chilworth. He may have been at Chilworth as early as 1651 and certainly by March 1653, when he was having difficulty getting carriages in the Guildford area to take his powder to Portsmouth.[1] The First Dutch War, one of three conflicts in the second half of the seventeenth century between the maritime powers of England and the Netherlands, was fought in 1652–4. Dewye later stated that he had made 150 barrels of powder a week and sent 1800 barrels to Portsmouth during this war. He left Chilworth and moved to gunpowder mills at Carshalton in 1661.[2]

Sir Jonas Moore stated in his survey of the Chilworth mills that the Middle Works had been built by Vincent Randyll in the First Dutch War. Randyll petitioned the Admiralty for a contract at this time and formed a partnership with George Duncombe and John Woodroffe, but this partnership does not seem to have achieved immediate success. Randyll only became a regular supplier during the Second Dutch War of 1665–7 and then continued until his death in 1673.[3] Gunpowder production at Chilworth temporarily ceased at this point as Morgan Randyll, Vincent's son, chose not to continue the business but to follow a political career as MP for Guildford.

With the building of the Middle Works, the basic layout of mills and watercourses at Chilworth, as it can still be seen today, was complete. The main features are shown in the sketch map for 1654 in figure 4.

John Aubrey, in his *History of Surrey*, gave a well-known description of the mills in the late seventeenth century and mentioned some of the processes of manufacture:[4]

> In this little pleasant Valley, the Springs serve not only to water the Grounds, but for the driving of 18 Mills, 5 whereof were blown up in a little more than half a Years Time. 'Tis a little Commonwealth of Powdermakers, who are as black as Negroes. Here is a Nursery of Earth for the making of Salt-Petre. There is also here a Boyling-House, where the Salt-Petre is made, and shoots; a Corneing House, and separating and finishing Houses, all very well worth the seeing of the Ingenious. I had almost forgot the Brimstone Mill, and the Engine to search it.

Aubrey's description is by no means complete and refers mainly to the preparation of the ingredients. Saltpetre is being obtained from compost and refined in the boiling house. It is there dissolved in water which is boiled down and left to cool so that crystals form or 'shoot'. The 'brimstone mill and the engine to search it' is probably a set of water-powered mill stones for pulverising sulphur. Similar equipment would also be needed to grind the charcoal and the three ingredients would then be thoroughly mixed together in the required proportions and moistened before being incorporated in the 18 mills.

Incorporating mills in this period were water-powered pestles and mortars, usually termed stamp or pestle mills and sometimes trough mills, because the massive timber beams housing the mortars were known as troughs. They became obsolete in Britain in the eighteenth century but continued in some parts of the world and figure 9 shows an example in Greece, photographed before its restoration as a museum exhibit. The pestles were raised by tappets on a horizontal beam, which was rotated by a waterwheel, and then fell under their own weight on to the charge in the mortars. There could be two or more such beams geared to one waterwheel, so that a mill might be described as having two or three troughs. Incorporation continued

Figure 9   Water-powered pestle mill in Greece, photographed in 1995 prior to its restoration at the Open Air Water Power Museum at Dimitsana, Peloponnese. The pestle mills at Chilworth were probably of similar construction but housed in a timber building. Composite photograph by Pantelis Magoulas from the ETBA Cultural Foundation Photolibrary Collection, Athens.

for many hours, with the charge being re-arranged and moistened from time to time.

The next process Aubrey refers to is corning, or forming the powder into grains. This process was introduced in the sixteenth century because loose powder did not perform consistently and its constituents tended to separate out in transit. It involved forcing the damp incorporated powder through sieves, at first by hand and later by means of a shaking frame set in motion by a water wheel.

The separating house would have been for separating the grains of powder from loose dust, probably by tumbling it in a mesh-covered reel. Drawings of corning and dusting equipment dating from the late eighteenth century are shown in chapter 8. The powder, which was still damp, would have been dried in a heated stove and packed in barrels. Besides the process buildings, there would have been stores and workshops and a watch house for security and for the workmen to spend periods of inactivity while the mills were left working.

Details of small equipment, including coppers for boiling saltpetre liquor and a large number of small pans for setting it out to crystallise, come from the inventory of 1682[5] reproduced as figure 10.

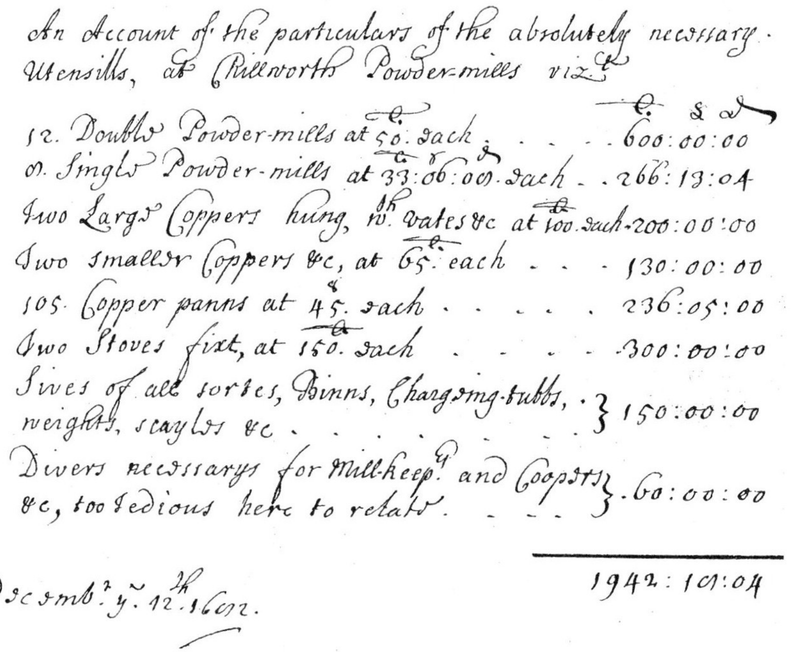

An Account of the particulars of the absolutely necessary.
Utensills, at Chillworth Powder-mills viz.

12. Double Powder-mills at 50. each 600:00:00
08. Single Powder-mills at 33:06:00. each - . .266:13:04
Two Large Coppers hung, w. vates &c at 100. each 200:00:00
Two smaller Coppers &c, at 65. each - . . 130:00:00
105. Copper panns at 45. each 236:05:00
Two Stoves fixt, at 150. each . . . . - 300:00:00
Sives of all sortes, Binns, Chargeing-tubbs, . } 150:00:00
weights, scayles &c . . . . . . }
Divers necessarys for mill-keep.' and Coopers} 60:00:00
&c, too tedious here to relate. . . }

Decembr y.̃ 12. 1682.

1942: 18:04

Figure 10 An account of the particulars of the absolutely necessary utensills at Chillworth Powder-mills vizt.

	£	s	d
12 Double Powder-mills at £50 each	600	00	00
8 single powder-mills at £33 06s 08d each	266	13	04
Two large coppers hung, with vates etc at £100 each	200	00	00
Two smaller coppers etc at £65 each	130	00	00
105 copper panns at 45s each	236	05	00
Two stoves fixt at £150 each	300	00	00
Sives of all sortes, binns, chargeing tubbs, weights, scayles etc	150	00	00
Divers necessarys for mill-keep[ing?] and coopers etc,			
too tedious here to relate	60	00	00
	£1942	18	04

December the 12th 1682

Reproduced by permission of the Staffordshire & Stoke on Trent Archive Service (StRO D742/M/1/33).

Sir Jonas Moore's survey of 1677 describes the lay-out of the site at that date, with the number of mills in each of the three works, the number of troughs in each, and the names by which they were known.[6] The Lower Works comprised the following:

Chillworth Mill with two troughs; Copps Mill with two troughs — these

stood 'upon the pond before the hop ground'. A further six mills
followed 'each lower than the other upon a Cutt from the Pond above'.
They were:
One mill for grinding Coal and Brimstone;
Wood Pile Mill has two troughs;
Dust Mill has two troughs, the bank against it in decay;
Double Mill 3 troughs;
Chattering Mill 2 troughs;
Shifford Mill 2 troughs.

The mill for grinding coal and brimstone was for preparing these
two ingredients — 'coal' at this period meant charcoal, whereas pit
coal was commonly referred to as 'sea coal' in the south of England
because it came by sea from Newcastle.

Shifford Mill is probably a mis-spelling of Shalford Mill, showing
that the last of the series of mills on the leat below the mill pond
was over the parish boundary between Shalford and St Martha's.

Also at the Lower Works there were two storehouses, a brick
dwelling house for the steward to live in, some pasture and meadow
and a 'Square convenient by place where all Offices for refining Salt
Petre, and other Labourers about the Corning and makeing Powder
are built'.

At the Middle Works there had evidently been some accidents as
there were:

The Lower Mill, 3 troughs, blown up;
The Cole and Brimstone Mill;
The Midle Mill 3 troughs;
Randills Mill, 3 troughs, blown up;
The Upper Mill 3 troughs.

The survey noted that the 'Upper Work was once a Compleat
Work of it selfe, had its watch-house, Stove, and Corning-house,
and wanted nothing but a Coale and Brimstone Mill' which Sir
Jonas proposed should be 'made and compleated, and this work
kept intire, and in good repair, against such time as there shall
be necessity to work it'. It had, besides 2 watch-houses, these
several mills:

Twist Mill, 3 troughs Stands on Mr Randills ground, and on the new
Cutt which is above halfe a mile long;
The Lower Mill 3 troughs Stands on Mr Randills ground;

The first Mill on the parson of Aldbury's Ground had 3 troughs and is
blown up;
The 2nd Mill on the said parsons ground has 3 troughs;
The 3rd and uppermost of the said parsons Mills has 3 troughs;
Upper Mill 3 troughs stands on Mr Randill's ground.

The Ordnance Board in 1677 wanted the Chilworth mills made
serviceable again, in case they were needed for another war, and Sir
Jonas's report was encouraging:

> The Powder Mills at Chilworth being all over Shott Mills[7] they may be
> constantly kept at work there being water sufficient in dry years, and
> may be made goe in the greatest frosts, and can not be stoppt by back
> water, do stand in the most commodious place imaginable both for deliv-
> ery of Powder either at London or Portsmouth, and certainly if to beginn
> to be built would cost many thousand pounds, which his Majesty's Pre-
> decessors and himself have Collaterally payd; It can not therefor, but be
> highly advantagious for his Majesty and the whole kingdome, that these
> works, and the Courses for water be kept in good repair, it being certain
> that by them near 1000 barrels of Gunpowder may be made every
> month.

Sir Polycarpus Wharton

Sir Jonas Moore's report persuaded a leading powdermaker, Sir
Polycarpus Wharton to take a lease of the mills for 21 years and
invest large sums of his own money in repairing them, so that they
became by far the largest gunpowder mills in the country.

Powdermaking was a dangerous, insecure and unpredictable
occupation. Demand fluctuated and governments, while anxious
to ensure that there was enough manufacturing capacity in time
of war, were notoriously bad at paying their bills. Many powdermakers suffered financial hardship for this reason, as Samuel
Cordwell had during the Civil War. Sir Polycarpus was in dispute
with the Ordnance about the settlement of the accounts of his
father, Sir George Wharton, who had been treasurer and paymas-
ter to the Board, as well as over the terms and honouring of his
own contracts, by which he claimed to have suffered to the extent
of £24,000. He found himself in a debtor's prison by 1710 and
an account of his grievances was published in a pamphlet entitled
'The Hard Case of Sir Polycarpus Wharton, Baronet'. This was
reprinted in John Aubrey's *History of Surrey*, which was published
a few years later in 1719.[8]

Notes

1. *Gunpowder Mills: Documents*, 29.
2. *Gunpowder Mills: Documents*, chapter 3.
3. *VCH*, vol.2, 322; Fairclough, K F, 'The Hard Case of Sir Polycarpus Wharton', *SyAC*, vol.83 (1996), 125–35, at p.126. Details of the involvement of Dewye and Randyll at Chilworth needs clarification and research is continuing.
4. Aubrey, vol.4, 56–7.
5. StRO, Dartmouth Papers, D742/M/1/33.
6. StRO, Dartmouth Papers, D742/M/1/13.
7. The water enters an overshot waterwheel just over the top. Overshot wheels are generally more efficient than undershot wheels, which the water enters near the bottom, or breastshot wheels which are intermediate.
8. Aubrey, vol.4, 58–65; *VCH*, vol.2, 326; Fairclough, 'The Hard Case of Sir Polycarpus Wharton' (see note 3).

5

Chilworth Manor in the Early Eighteenth Century

After Sir Polycarpus Wharton left Chilworth, the gunpowder mills went into decline. The Upper site at Postford was abandoned altogether and in 1704 the Lower Works were converted to paper-making. Only the Middle Works continued to produce gunpowder and it was not until the late nineteenth century that they expanded to become a site of national importance again.

The owner of the manor, Morgan Randyll, who had followed a political career as MP for Guildford, had become heavily in debt through contesting elections and in 1720 sold the estate. The purchaser was Richard Houlditch, who was a director of the South Sea Company. His property was seized when the bubble burst and was put up for sale by the trustees. A detail of the sale particulars is shown in figure 11. Sarah Duchess of Marlborough appears to have used the opportunity of the South Sea Bubble to acquire a number of estates at this time, and sent her agent Robert Barnes to inspect and report on the manor of Chilworth. He was not enthusiastic:

Computation by Robert Barnes of 33 acres late Morgan Randyll Esq. Chilworth lyes 2 miles south-east from Guildford in the County of Surrey, situated in an Ugly Dale. There is 4 powder mills and 2 paper mills which last will cost to repair £600. Mills are the worst estates and often come to nothing.

The Duchess however ignored his advice and purchased the manor. On her death it passed to her grandson John Spencer and it remained in the Spencer family until 1796. Many documents relating to Chilworth are therefore among archives of the Spencer family in

A
PARTICULAR
OF THE FREEHOLD
ESTATE
OF
RICHARD HOULDITCH, Efq;

(One of the late Directors of the

SOUTH-SEA COMPANY.)

Situate in the feveral Parifhes of *Chilworth,*
St. Martha, and *Elftead,* near *Guildford,*
in the County of *Surry.*

To be Sold by Cant or Auction to the beft Bidder, in
the Hall of the *South-Sea* Houfe, on *Wednefday*
the 20th Day of *November* next, at Ten of the
Clock in the Forenoon.

Figure 11   Extract from sale particulars of Chilworth Manor, 1723 (retouched).
Reproduced by permission of the Northamptonshire Record Office (SOX 488).

the Northamptonshire Record Office and the British Library.[1] They
include the 1728 survey of the estate, which is mentioned in connection with mill sites in chapter 3 and of which a detail is reproduced
in chapter 7. This shows the Upper Works derelict, with the ponds
nearly dry, the Middle Works still leased as powder mills, the paper
mills at the Lower Works and the use of land for woods, pastures,
meadows and growing hops.

Flowing the Meadows
The Duchess's survey also shows the ponds and watercourses, much

as they remain today, including a new system of artificial water channels which were used for irrigating the meadows. This was a method of agricultural improvement introduced in England in the seventeenth century which involved seasonally running water over the land — known as 'flowing' or 'floating' the meadows — to extend the growing season so that an extra crop of hay could be produced. It was first introduced at Chilworth at the end of the seventeenth century. A lease to the powdermaker dated 1719 explains that it had been done in and about the Middle Works for 21 years and that the water from the Postford Stream had been used in this way for ten years past.

The Postford Stream is an artificial channel which comes off the old mill-stream for Twist Mill and runs westwards, connecting several springs, to Tangley Mere and beyond. It can be seen today for example at the rear of the Percy Arms public house. Secondary channels, controlled by sluice-gates, led from this main channel to the meadows and finally into the mill leats of the gunpowder and paper mills.

The 1719 lease makes provision for the operation to be carried out four times a year: once between Michaelmas (29 September) and 31 December for three weeks at least, once in April or May for three weeks, and twice after hay harvest and before Michaelmas for 48 hours each time.[2]

A Visitor from America

In 1735 a young colonial American visited Chilworth and recorded his impressions in the diary he kept during his nine-month stay in England. Robert Hunter Morris came to London as companion and secretary to his father, Lewis Morris, an attorney who was acting as agent for a group of New Yorkers. Lewis and Robert had family links with the powdermaker Thomas Pearse and he took them to see the powder mills at Faversham and Chilworth which he had recently acquired.[3] They travelled down from London to Chilworth on a Saturday in July:

Saturday, July 19, 1735. I rosse at 4 and read till 9, when I shaved and dress'd. About 10 Mr. Pearse came, with whom we were Engaged to go to Guilford to see his powder mills . . . We had a fine day to Travell in. We dined at Cobham at Mr. Pearses Expence and Got to His mills about 9 o'Clock . . .

Sunday, July 20, 1735. Chilworth, near Guilford. I ross at 9 after Every-body Elce, and, Having brakefasted and dress'd, we went to view the mills, which took us till noon. We saw four pair of large bed[*sic*] stones and as many bed Stones for them to run on. The runners were 6 foot diamiter and the bed Stones something bigger. These stones were not yet put up. We saw the same conveniences for making and Corning powder here as at Feversham. We dined and sat the afternoon in the house with two countrymen. The one rented the paper mills Just by Mr. Pearses House, which we were also to see in the morning. The other lived in the mantion House, that being the House wherin I was informed Randall Vane was borne. These Countrymen seemed to make byt a serul [servile?] apearance and not a bit better than countrymen usually do with us in America. We supped on some frogs, which one of the gentlemen would not Eat, it being the first time He or any of the Company had Seen any Eat before. Mr. Pearse Eat most of them HimSelf. We went to bed about 10.

Monday, July 21, 1735. Chilworth. I ross at 6 and went out in order to Catch some fish. I had not been out long before it began to rain, Which, before I got home, wet me pretty much. I shifted, brakefasted, and, it Continuing to rain, we stayd at Home till about 6, when Mr. Dabner and I went to see a learge pond about a mile from the House, but, in going thether, we were taken in a shoar of rain, which continued for some time and obliged us to take Sanctuary in a new stable, building for a country farmer. Here we found the Carpenters at work. I asked them many Questions about their wages, which they told me was 18d per day with small bear and to find themselves. We finding the rain Continue, we returned without Seeing the pond. Went to rest.

Tuesday, July 22, 1735. I rosse at 6, as did the rest of the family. We drest and brakefasted and then set out for London. We had some diffi-culty in getting the shase from the house to the publick road, which at last we Accomplishd. I rode Almost as far as Cobbham and then sent back the Horse . . .

Besides his observations on Chilworth society and customs, Robert Hunter Morris shows that improvements had been made to the estate — Postford Pond had evidently been repaired since the Duchess of Marlborough's survey of 1728 — and that new techno-logy was being installed at the gunpowder works.[4] Unfortunately, the intended visit to the paper mills is not described in his diary. The house where his party stayed was probably the one now known as The Old Manor House, on the corner of Blacksmith Lane and Dork-ing Road, which was formerly known as Powder Mill House. Per-haps he went fishing in the Chilworth mill pond, or in Tangley Mere, which were both nearby. The large fishing pond a mile from the house must be Postford Pond and the farm where he sheltered from the rain fits the location of Lockner Farm.

*   *   *

In spite of his opinion of the Tillingbourne valley as an 'ugly dale', Robert Barnes took a 21-year lease of Lockner Farm in 1738 and one hopes settled there contentedly.[5]

Notes

1. NRO, Spencer papers (SOX 488); British Library Manuscripts, General Survey of Chillworth St Martha, 1728 (Althorp Papers, PG4, General).

2. NRO, SOX 488, Abstract of lease 1766, pp.2–3. Details of flowing the meadows in the nineteenth century are given in a document of 1805 discussed in chapter 10 and in a lease of 28 Sept 1832 (Lambeth Archives 3057).

3. Morris, Robert Hunter, 'An American in London, 1735–1736: the diary of Robert Hunter Morris', edited by Beverley McAnear, *Pennsylvania Magazine of History and Biography*, vol. 64 (1940), 164–217, 356–406.

4. See chapter 7.

5. NRO, SOX 488, Abstract of lease 1766, pp.9–13.

6

Making Paper by Hand

Paper is known to have been made in China by the second century BC[1] but it took over a thousand years for the invention to spread to Europe. In about AD 800, using captured Chinese papermakers, the Arabs set up paper manufactories in the Near East. The craft spread to Morocco by 1100 and thence through Spain to Europe. However it was not until the late fifteenth century that the first paper mill was built in England. This was near Hertford but the venture was short-lived and the industry was not permanently established in England until the late sixteenth century when mills opened at Maidstone and Dartford in Kent. Papermaking then developed steadily, particularly around London. By 1650 there were over forty mills in England and by the end of the century about a hundred.[2]

Early paper mills needed water-power, clean water, a ready supply of rags as raw materials and a market for the paper. Papermakers therefore looked for sites on rural streams near large centres of population. The best sites were already occupied by other industries, especially corn milling. However, near the chalk hills of south-east England, around London, some sites were becoming available in the early seventeenth century because of the decline of the local woollen industry and the consequent closure of fulling mills. Indeed the water-powered stocks used for fulling cloth operated in a similar way to the stampers of paper mills.[3]

The earliest known reference to papermaking in Surrey is contained in John Aubrey's *History* of the county, published in 1719 but written mainly in the 1670s.[4] In his description of Godalming

he refers to paper being made in Surrey in the reign of James I, who
died in 1625. He described the town as follows:

> In this Place are one Grist-Mill, two Paper-Mills, and three Corn-Mills;
> and Sir Richard Baker in his Chronicle tells us, that in the Reign of King
> James I, coarse Paper, commonly call'd whited brown Paper, was first
> made in England, especially in Surrey and about Windsor; and this Place,
> I have frequently heard, bore the Bell from all this County, for its excel-
> lency in the Manufacture.

There is no supporting evidence however that paper mills were
established in the Godalming area until about 1660 when parts of
Eashing and Catteshall mills were converted to papermaking.[5] In the
meantime a paper mill had been built at Stoke-next-Guildford and
the first lease probably dates from the 1630s.[6] Stoke is therefore the
first Surrey paper mill for which documentary information is available. Figure 12 shows it as it was in about 1800.

Figure 12   The paper mill at Stoke-next-Guildford, based on a drawing of about
1800 by W C Beauties held at the Minet Library, Lambeth. Stoke is the earliest
paper mill in Surrey for which documentary evidence is known. Charles Ball, who
moved to Surrey from Northamptonshire in 1790, was at Stoke before he became
papermaker at Chilworth and then Albury (chapter 9). The drawing shows the
clasped-arm timber waterwheel which powered the beating engines or Hollanders
on the ground floor, a small building to its left where the papermaker or vatman
probably worked, and the characteristic shuttered drying lofts. The papermaker's
house is seen at the right. Drawing by Alan Crocker.

These early paper mills must have been successful as others were established in the district. The names, active periods and locations (national grid reference) of those on the Tillingbourne and nearby on the Wey are summarised below:

Albury Park	Tillingbourne (TQ 162 479)	1790–1810
Bower's, Worplesdon[7]	River Wey (TQ 012 529)	1716–1790
Byfleet	River Wey (TQ 072 606)	1673–1703
Catteshall, Godalming	River Wey (SU 982 443)	1661–1928
Chilworth Great	Tillingbourne (TQ 024 475)	1704–1870
Chilworth Little	Tillingbourne (TQ 024 475)	1704–1829
Eashing, Godalming	River Wey (SU 946 437)	1658–1889
Postford Lower	Tillingbourne (TQ 039 480)	1809–1875
Postford Upper	Tillingbourne (TQ 041 480)	1809–1830
Stoke, Guildford	River Wey (SU 998 510)	1636–1869
Westbrook, Godalming	River Wey (SU 967 442)	1732?–1842
Woking	River Wey (TQ 015 565)	1840–1895

At first these mills made coarse brown paper or the 'whited-brown paper' which Aubrey mentions, the better quality writing paper being imported from the Continent. Then in the late seventeenth century many French and Dutch papermakers came to England and the Company of White Paper Makers in England was incorporated and granted a monopoly to produce writing and printing papers.[8] Byfleet was one of the mills they operated.[9] It was visited by John Evelyn on 24 April 1678 and he recorded his observations in his diary:

> They cull the rags which are linen for white paper, woollen for brown; they then stamp them in troughs to a pap with pestles or hammers like the powder-mills, then put it into a vessel of water, in which they dip a frame closely wired with wire as small as a hair and as close as a weaver's reed; on this they take up the pap, the superfluous water draining through the wire; this they dexterously turn, shake out like a pancake on a smooth board between two pieces of flannel, then press it between a great press, the flannel sucking out the moisture; then taking it out, they ply and dry it on strings, as they dry linen in the laundry; then dip it in alum water, lastly polish, and make it up in quires. They put some gum in the water in which they macerate the rags. The mark we find in the sheets is formed in the wire.[10]

Evelyn described the processes of papermaking briefly and in layman's terms. The paper was made from rags which were sorted, cut (figure 13), washed and left to ferment in water. White linen or cotton rags were used for good quality paper and coarse rags for brown paper. They were then placed in a trough and pounded by water-powered hammers or stampers which, as Evelyn observed, were similar to those used in powder mills (figure 9). This produced a creamy pulp known as stuff. In the first half of the eighteenth century new, more efficient, machines for making pulp were introduced from Holland and gradually replaced the earlier stampers. A Hollander, illustrated in figure 18 in chapter 7, consisted of an oval trough, about 3 metres long, around which a mixture of water and rags was churned and macerated by an adjustable iron roller with projecting blades.

The pulp or stuff was transferred to a vat where it was kept luke-warm and agitated to keep the fibres in suspension. Individual sheets of paper were made, as shown in figure 14, by a vatman who dipped a mould, consisting of a rectangular wooden frame with a cover of wire, into the stuff. He lifted it out, with a slight tilt to avoid suction, and gave it a series of deft shakes so that the water drained away, leaving a layer of matted fibres on the mesh. The edge of the sheet was formed by a wooden frame called a deckle which was placed around the mould before it was dipped into the vat. The wet sheet of paper was turned over on to a piece of felt by a second workman known as the coucher who built up a stack or post of 144 sheets of paper interleaved with felt. This was placed in the wet press to squeeze out as much water as possible and a third man, the layer, then separated the sheets of paper and hung them over ropes in a loft

Figure 13   Cutting rags for papermaking, from the *Cyclopaedia of Arts and Manufactures*, 1854.

Figure 14 Papermaking by hand, from *The Penny Magazine*, 1833. A vatman and coucher are working together with a pair of moulds. The vatman on the right is dipping his mould fitted with a deckle into the stuff. After this he will lift it out, not quite horizontally, shake it, remove the deckle, place the mould containing a wet piece of paper on the bridge across the vat, take a second mould from the bridge, place the deckle around it and repeat the process. Meanwhile the coucher on the left is placing a piece of felt on a sheet of paper at the top of a pile of alternating paper and felts. After this he will take the mould, which is resting against a post called an asp on the bridge, turn it over to deposit the paper on the felt, place the empty mould on the bridge, take the full mould and rest it against the asp and repeat the process. Note the steam pipe leading to the vat to keep the stuff warm and the characteristic paper hats worn by the workmen.

to dry (figure 15). The drying lofts of paper mills had characteristic shuttered walls for ventilation, as shown in figure 12.

The sheets were flattened in another press and polished in a large finishing room called the salle or sol. Paper for writing also had to be sized and this was done either by mixing size with the pulp or dipping dry sheets into a tub of size.

The watermark in the paper was formed by a wire design fixed to the mesh of the mould, as shown in figure 16. The mesh of a traditional 'laid' mould consisted of hundreds of parallel wires about 0.5mm in diameter and about the same distance apart. These were tied together about every 25mm by a pair of flexible wires to form a flat sheet. The whole was then tied down with fine wire to wooden ribs fixed across the back of the mould.

Figure 15 Drying loft of a paper mill. This example is at the Richard-de-Bas papermaking mill museum at Ambert, Puy-de-Dôme, France. Photo by Glenys Crocker.

Figure 16 Detail of a watermark device, attached with stitches of very fine wire to the cover of a mould. Note the straight horizontal laid wires, the twisted vertical chain wires and, behind these, the wooden ribs of the mould to which the chain wires are themselves attached with fine wire. This example, dating from 1812, is from a mould of the Haslemere papermaker James Simmons. A tracing of the complete device is shown in figure 38. Courtesy of Haslemere Educational Museum. Photo by the University of Surrey.

The characteristic marks produced by these wires in the paper are known as laid and chain lines and these cause a slight unevenness in the surface. In the middle of the eighteenth century James Whatman, a leading papermaker in Kent, developed the 'wove' mould of fine woven wire which leaves only an indistinct impression resembling fabric in the paper. Paper made by Whatman on this type of mould was used by the celebrated typographer John Baskerville to print his high quality books. The use of smooth wove paper in his *Virgil* of 1757 was acclaimed universally.[11]

Notes

1. Needham, J (ed), *Science and Civilisation in China*, vol.5 (1): *Paper and Printing* (Cambridge, 1986).
2. Shorter, *Paper Making*, 13–34.
3. Shorter, *Paper Making*, 32.
4. Aubrey, vol.4, 16.
5. *VCH*, vol.2, 418–9; Crocker, A & G, *Catteshall Mill* (SyAS Research Volume 8, 1981), 5–6.
6. British Library, Add MSS 6174: Stoughton Manuscript, f.20.
7. Bower's Mill was near Burpham, 4 km north-east of Guildford, and is marked 'Paper Mill' in figure 1, but incorrectly shown 1 km downstream from its actual site.
8. Shorter, *Paper Making*, 24.
9. Crocker, A, 'The Paper Mills of Surrey', *Surrey History*, vol.4 no.1 (1989–90), 49–64, at 55–6.
10. *VCH*, vol.2, 418.
11. Hills, R L, *Papermaking in Britain 1488–1988* (Athlone Press, 1988).

7

Chilworth Paper Mills
in the Eighteenth Century

The Lower Works of the Chilworth gunpowder mills were converted into paper mills in 1704. The deeds appear to be lost but the date is known from a court case of 1817, which is discussed in chapter 10, and is consistent with a lease, assumed to be for 21 years, which terminated in 1725. Two paper mills, known as Chilworth Great and Chilworth Little were established but the former, which had two vats, was sometimes described as being two mills under one roof.[1]

When the estate was offered for sale by the trustees of the South Sea Company in 1720, the particulars referred to 'A Paper Mill' which was untenanted but considered to have a rental value of £20 a year, although formerly let at £35. This must have been Chilworth Little Mill. Another entry is to 'The Paper Mills', clearly Chilworth Great, with associated land amounting to about 18 acres, which was in the occupation of Thomas Hillier at a yearly rent of £77. In 1716 Hillier was described as a papermaker in the Shalford parish registers and he and his family were also at Bower's Mill near Burpham in Guildford and later at Downside Mill near Cobham.[2]

Other names of papermakers in these registers include Thomas Eedes 1708–26, Edward West 1713, John Maidman 1716, 1722, John Adams 1721, Thomas Maidman 1722, Simon Ayres 1724 and Salter 1724. Probably they were all associated with Chilworth as both paper mills were near the boundary between the parishes of St Martha's and Shalford. Indeed, the dwelling house of the Great Paper Mill was in Shalford and during the nineteenth century the mill itself was to expand across this boundary. However, some of the names could have been associated with Catteshall mill in Godalming and Simon Ayres and John Maidman are also known at Stoke and Bower's mills respectively.

When the Duchess of Marlborough was considering purchasing Chilworth Manor in 1723 her agent Robert Barnes reported that the paper mills would cost £600 to repair, which indicates that they had run into serious difficulties. In 1725 she leased the two mills for 21 years to Thomas Watkins at a rent of £110 a year with only £230 allowed for repairs. The lease states that the previous occupiers were Thomas Maidman, John Baldwin and Thomas Hillier. This is the only known reference to Baldwin. Watkins is reputed to have brought improvements in papermaking to England from the Continent and in particular, in 1713, he is said to have introduced the beating engine or Hollander. However in 1723, described as a stationer of London and a papermaker of Longford Mill in Middlesex, he had become bankrupt.[3] Unfortunately the lease provides no information about the equipment in the mills.

The detailed survey of the Chilworth Manor estate which was prepared for the Duchess in 1728 names the tenants of 'The Great and Little Paper Mills' as 'Mr Gay and Mr Wadking'. Gay was presumably the Mr Guy who paid rent to Thomas Norgate, the Duchess's agent, in 1728 but is otherwise unknown. He may have been a businessman who brought capital to the partnership rather than a papermaker. Wadking was clearly Thomas Watkins.

A detail of the survey, showing the two paper mills, together with part of the adjacent gunpowder works, is shown as figure 17. It uses the prefix F for the paper mills and G for the powder mills. 'Paper Mills Lane' leads northwards to the rectangular 'Mill Pond'. The symbol 'F' immediately to the north-west of the pond refers to the property of the Great Paper Mill consisting of four buildings labelled 1–4. These are the dwelling house and its associated garden, the mill itself powered by three waterwheels, the drying house alongside the mill by the dam, and the small square rag house where rags for making paper were stored. The Little Paper Mill (F6) is south-west of the Great Mill, the two waterwheels being fed by a 75-metre leat from the south corner of the pond and also a channel coming in the opposite direction from the network of watercourses which was used for flowing the meadows. It had a hop garden, with the poles represented symbolically, and its own drying house (F8). The papermakers also held several fields and other land, including the orchard (F5) and 'The Corning-house Plot Pasture' (F15), named after one of the

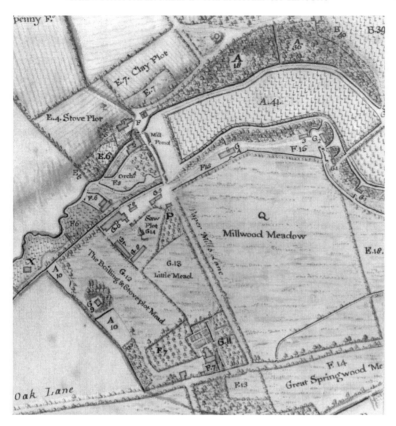

Figure 17 Detail of the 'General Survey of Chillworth St Martha' prepared in 1728 for Sarah, Duchess of Marlborough, showing Chilworth paper mills and the adjacent gunpowder mills, hop gardens and farmland. The Great Paper Mill, with its dwelling house, drying house and rag house, labelled indistinctly F2, Fl, F3 and F4 respectively are clustered around the west side of the mill pond, and the Little Paper Mill, with its drying house labelled F6 & F8 are south-west of this. By permission of the British Library (Althorp Papers, PG4, General).

process buildings of the gunpowder works. These also include incorporating mills (G1), a charcoal and brimstone mill (G2), a corning house (G4) and a saltpetre boiling house (G6).

It appears that Guy and Watkins were unable to make a success of papermaking at Chilworth and in 1733 the Duchess leased the Great and Little mills for 21 years to Richard Boxall for £112 8s a year. In 1732, when he was a papermaker at Westbrook Mill in Godalming, Boxall had married into the Hall family, successful papermakers at Eashing Mill since 1796. His wife Anne was the daughter of Thomas Hall I and sister of Thomas Hall II.[4] The lease, this time, provides some interesting information about the equipment in the mills. There were drying houses, three engines, eight mortars and all the wheels and implements. The engines would have been Hollander beating engines, which must have been introduced by Watkins, and the mortars were the old-fashioned stamp mills for converting rags into pulp.

Events at the mills in the mid-eighteenth century included an explosion at the gunpowder works in 1755 in which a body was blown over a new paper mill.[5] In 1756 the young William Bray, aged 20, who was later to complete Owen Manning's monumental *History of Surrey* and edit John Evelyn's Diaries, recorded a visit to the paper mill in his own diary.[6] In 1760 or 1761 there was another explosion at the gunpowder works and two workers at the paper mill, Gadd and Collis, were killed and many others injured. The walls of the paper mill were split almost from top to bottom.[7] Papermakers named in the Shalford parish registers in the mid-eighteenth century, most of whom were probably skilled workmen, include Maidman, William Blackwell and Richard Rose, in the period 1739–45, and Daniel Byrch, Edward Cheesemore and James Faukner in 1741–61. Also, Robert Wilson, a papermaker, was married at St Martha's church in 1744.[8]

Richard Boxall remained at Chilworth from 1733 until he died. He was succeeded in 1763 by Thomas Hall III, who was the nephew of Thomas Hall II and had been the papermaker at Eashing Mill since 1756. He leased the mills from Earl Spencer, the grandson of the Duchess of Marlborough. The term was again 21 years, the annual rent had increased to £137 8s and the following inventory was taken:

A Schedule or Inventory of the Engines, Wheels, going Gears, Goods, Implements amd Things belonging to the Paper Mills at Chilworth, taken by Wm Shipton, 19 June 1763. (NRO SOX488)

The Great Mill
   In the Engine House. Three engines for grinding rags, all the carcases and carriages of heart of oak plank, three rolls of elm, three spindles, 36 steel bars in each roll in all 108 bars, 3 steel plates under the rolls, 14 steel bars in each of the plates, 5 small brass cocks, 3 large brass cocks, 3 leaden pipes about 4 feet long each and 2 inch bore and a half stuff chest, six brasses for the spindles.
   In the Workhouse. Two vats with two iron pans, two grates and covers, five presses, four brass hooks, two winches with ropes and levers to them, eight press blocks, two stuff chests about 15 feet of [. . .] lead pipe of 1 inch bore and a small brass cock.

In the Sizing House etc 3 brick cisterns and a small boarded cistern, in the orchard a leaden pipe from the brick cisterns to the sizing copper in the sizing house about 70 feet long 2 inches bore with a large brass cock, one press in the sizing house. The bottom of the conduit laid with lead.

Three water wheels 10 feet diameter, six gudgeons and six brasses, three cogg wheels and three swimming wheels 9 feet diameter and 8 inches thick, three pair of heads three brasses to the swimming wheel all heart of oak timber.

The Little Mill

Two engines for grinding rags the carcases and carriages of heart of oak plank, two rolls of elm, two spindles to the rolls, 36 steel bars in each roll weight, 2 steel plates under the rolls weight, 13 steel bars in each plate, 4 brasses for the spindles, a boarded water cistern, a half stuff chest and 2 shoots or troughs.

In the Vat House. One vat with an iron pan grate and cover, three presses, two press hooks, one winch rope and lever, four press blocks, one stuff chest about 15 feet of lead pipe to the vat one inch bore and a small brass cock.

In the Chopping House, a cutting box, about 4 feet of lead pipe 2 inches bore and a large brass cock.

Two water wheels 11 feet in diameter, four gudgeons, four brasses, 2 cog wheels 8 feet diameter and 8 inches thick, two swimming wheels of the same dimensions, four gudgeons to the swimming wheels, two brasses and two pair of heads, all of heart of oak timber.

In all the Drying Houses belong to both mills, complete setts of trebles, lines and frames to hang the paper to dry.

Locks and keys to all the doors of the messuages or tenements and mills with the appurtenances.

And all and every other the wheels, going gears, utensils and implements belonging to the said mills together with the mill houses, messuages or tenements and other the premises in good and substantial repair.

[estimate for repairs]
Two new cogg wheels each ten feet diameter with timber workmanship and all materials included £20 0s 0d
Two new shafts, one 13 feet long the other 10 feet and a half long, in all 23 feet and a half, timber workmanship and all materials included £11 15s 0d
Elm boards to repair the water wheels about £5 4s 0d and workmanship in doing the said repairs about £5 0s 0d
To take out the old wheels and shafts and put in the new ones about 12 days work each for two men £3 12s 0d
To allow one shilling a foot for the elm that is wanted and sixteen pence a foot for the oak in the rough which is to be deducted out of the above account.

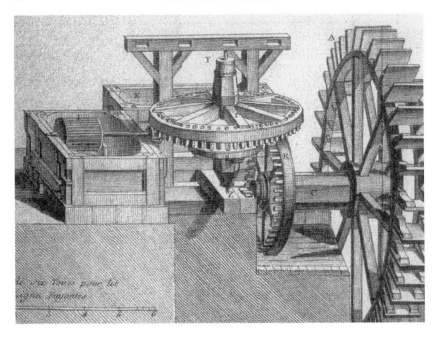

Figure 18 'Hollander' beating engines showing the drive from a waterwheel. Reproduced from Diderot's *Encyclopédie* (Paris, 1762–77). Courtesy of John Day.

This inventory shows that by 1763 all the stamp mills had been replaced by Hollander beating engines. The way in which these were linked to the waterwheels is shown in figure 18. The large horizontal gear wheel which in corn mills is known as a great spur wheel is called a 'swimming wheel' in the inventory. It engages with small pinion wheels which drive the rollers of the beating engines. In the figure the swimming wheel is driving two engines but in the inventory each of the five waterwheels has one swimming wheel and one engine. Other technical terms are explained in the glossary on pages 129–37.

In 1764 Thomas Hall III was left £100 by his aunt, Richard Boxall's widow Anne.[9] In the same year, described as a papermaker of Chilworth, he took out fire insurance on his paper mill at Eashing.[10] Then in 1777 two papermakers, James Gadd and George Chalcroft, ran away from Shalford.[11] Gadd may have been related to one of victims of the explosion at the gunpowder works in 1760 or 1761.

In 1781 the contents of Chilworth paper mills were insured by a new paper maker, Joseph Callow:

Joseph Callow at Chilworth in Surry, Papermaker. On his household goods in his dwelling house situate as aforesaid brick and tiled £150. On his utensils and stock viz: In the Paper Mill only near the house brick timber and tiled £450. In the raghouse only separate timber and tiled £50.[12]

Callow was also at Stoke paper mill and had a property known as 'The Cyder House', in Shalford parish near Guildford, which since 1721 had been linked to Stoke and Bower's mills.[13] At Chilworth he had a two-tenement property and ten acres of land on which he paid land tax, assessed at £20, until 1790.[14] He provided paper to his landlord, Earl Spencer, who in 1788 for example paid him £2 2s 0d for two reams of thick post and £2 2s 0d for three reams of foolscap.[15] Then in December 1790 William Tinkler, the owner of the gunpowder works wrote to his manager at Chilworth saying 'brown paper is wanted. If the paper mills are at work, perhaps you will be able to get some of the sort we used to have of Mr Callow'.[16] Clearly Callow had left the mills and indeed in 1791 he was declared bankrupt.[17]

Captain William Wilcox (or Wilcocks) and Charles Ball, who was also at Stoke and Albury Park mills, then became the papermakers. Ball wrote to Lord Spencer's agent in 1792 asking for timber to carry out repairs; his decorative signature is reproduced in figure 19. He dissolved the partnership with Wilcox in the following year[18] and Chilworth Mills were taken over by Edward Hughes.[19] Several examples of Hughes' watermarks have been found and are illustrated in figure 20. An Act of Parliament in 1794 enabled papermakers to reclaim excise duty on paper for certain uses if it was water-

Figure 19 Signature of Charles Ball senior. Reproduced by permission of the Northamptonshire Record Office (SOX 488).

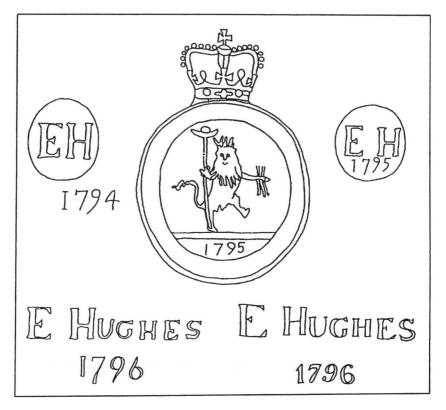

Figure 20   Watermarks of Edward Hughes.

marked with the year.[20] The rather crude graphical quality of the dates in Hughes's 1794 and 1795 paper suggests that they were added rather hurriedly but the 1796 watermark is much improved. Hughes attended a meeting of master papermakers in Guildford in 1796[21] and three years later he and Ball represented each other at further meetings.[22] In 1797 Hughes took out a new 38-year lease on the mills[23] but in practice soon left. Before taking up the story of his successors, Hugh Rowland, father and son, it is necessary to follow that of the powder mills through the eighteenth century.

Notes

1. Much of the information in this chapter is from documents in the Spencer Papers in the Northamptonshire Record Office (NRO, SOX 488) and from the General Survey of Chillworth St

   Martha, 1728, in the Althorp Papers in the British Library.
2. Information from parish registers in this chapter is from the Surrey section of Shorter, *Paper Mills*, 236–41.

3. Shorter, *Paper Making*, 40, 55.
4. For Hall family tree, see Crocker, A, 'The Paper Mills of Surrey, part 2', *Surrey History*, vol.4 no.4 (1992), 211–30, at p.214.
5. *Oxford Gazette & Reading Mercury*, 27 Oct 1755.
6. Bray, F E, *SyAC*, vol.46 (1938), 34.
7. See chapter 10.
8. Shorter, *Paper Mills*, 239.
9. Godalming Museum: Woods Hundred, vol.10, 272.
10. Guildhall Library, London, Sun Fire registers, 211856, 1 Sept 1764.
11. Shorter, *Paper Mills*, 239.
12. Guildhall Library, London, Sun Fire registers, vol.289, 438453, 20 Jan 1781.
13. SHC, Title deeds of Cyder House Shalford (G111/45),
14. SHC, Land tax (QS6/7, St Martha).
15. NRO, Spencer Papers, SOX 488.
16. SHC, Letter book of William Tinkler, 10 Dec 1790 (G132/1).
17. Simmons Collection.
18. Shorter, *Paper Mills*, 239.
19. SHC, Land tax to 1804 (QS6/7, St Martha).
20. Dagnall, H, *The Taxation of Paper in Great Britain* (Edgware, the author, 1998) 38–40.
21. SHC, Letter of 26 March 1796 on reverse of MS index to Russell's *History of Guildford* (SP 942 21, GU1).
22. Shorter, *Paper Mills*, 239.
23. SHC, Chilworth estate sale particulars, 1813 (G85/2/1(2) no.4).

8

Chilworth Gunpowder Mills
in the Eighteenth Century

When the Lower Works were converted to paper mills, England was engaged in the War of the Spanish Succession (1702–13). It is therefore puzzling that after Sir Polycarpus Wharton left there is no evidence of any powdermaker at Chilworth until 1716. In that year Francis Grueber is recorded as tenant of a piece of meadowland and in 1719 he took a lease of the Middle Works from Morgan Randyll.[1] As 'Mr Gaubar' he appears as tenant of the powder mills on the 1728 survey of Chilworth Manor.

Francis Grueber was a member of a family of Huguenot refugees who had left France in 1685 when Louis XIV revoked the Edict of Nantes, which had granted toleration to Protestants. The family had settled at Faversham in Kent, where they took over existing gunpowder mills and built up an expanding business. They supplied a large amount of powder for the war of 1702–13 and it may be that they were already using the Chilworth mills but that evidence has not yet been found.

Most of the gunpowder produced at this time was for military use and the chief customer was the government but there was a growing demand for gunpowder in overseas trade. London was the major port but first Bristol and then Liverpool developed as ports of the growing triangular trade between England, West Africa and the Americas. Iron goods and textiles, and to a minor extent gunpowder, were exchanged for slaves in Africa, the slaves were sold in the New World and the merchants returned to England with cargoes of tobacco and sugar.

When the war in Europe ended in 1713 a group of four gunpowder makers in the London area formed a partnership to reduce competition in the private market. Francis Grueber, of Faversham and Chilworth, was one of the four and the others were the powdermakers of East Molesey in Surrey, Bedfont in Middlesex and Waltham Abbey in Essex. In 1718 a law was passed to improve safety regulations for the storage and carriage of gunpowder in London. Powder makers were required to have magazines away from the city and the partners built theirs on the Thames Estuary at Barking Creek. Their successors in the partnership also built a magazine at Liverpool in 1737 to supply gunpowder to that city's expanding slave trade.

Francis Grueber was in financial difficulties by 1728 and entered into a partnership with Thomas Coram, the well-known philanthropist who established the London Foundling Hospital. Coram's business interests were in merchant shipping and he played an active role in transporting goods between the magazine at Barking and the mills at Chilworth and Faversham, as well as in financing and running the business.[2] By 1731 however Francis Grueber had sold out to Thomas Pearse, a Commissioner of the Navy who lived at Rochester.

It was Thomas Pearse who in 1735 took Lewis Morris and his son Robert Hunter Morris to see his powder mills at Chilworth.[3] As related in chapter 5, the young man reported in his diary that they saw four pairs of bed stones and runners which were 'not yet put up'. Evidently new technology was being adopted at Chilworth which involved replacing the old stamp mills for incorporating gunpowder with edge-runner mills. These consisted of horizontal bedstones on which runner stones rolled around on edge (figure 21), pressing and crushing the charge with a twisting action. Edge-runner mills were introduced in England in the late seventeenth century and were gradually adopted in place of stamp mills during the course of the eighteenth century. In 1772 stamp mills were made illegal in Great Britain, with some exemptions, because they were considered more dangerous, although they were preferred in France and North America until well into the nineteenth century and survived even longer in some parts of the world.

The Pearse family, father and then son, continued at Faversham and Chilworth and supplied about 30 per cent of the powder used by the Ordnance during the War of the Austrian Succession of 1740–48. They also obtained a large contract for repairing unserviceable powder after the war had ended. The younger Thomas Pearse was joined in partnership by William Stevens, gentleman of the parish of

Figure 21   Restored edge-runner incorporating mill at the Chart Mills gunpowder museum, Faversham. Drawing © Jack Salmon, for the Faversham Society.

St Christopher-le-Stocks, London, in 1746 and a new partnership agreement was signed in 1753 between them and Benjamin Pryce. On this occasion a detailed inventory was taken of the mills at Chilworth and Faversham, the partners' office in London, and their magazines at Barking Creek and Liverpool.[4]

The mills in 1753

The inventory shows that several grades of powder were being made for different markets. There were stocks of 'merchants powder' for the Africa trade, 'DS' or 'Double Seal' which was fine powder used for sport, and common powders of increasing fineness designated by the letters C&F, FF and FFF. The coarser products were probably sold for blasting in mines and quarries, a market which had been growing since blasting was introduced in England in the 1660s.

Of the raw materials for gunpowder, charcoal was brought to the mills ready-made. The woods of Surrey produced charcoal for a wide market in the eighteenth century; dealers included Smith & Son of Guildford and Youngs of Dorking. The trees were coppiced to produce long straight growths which were harvested periodically on a renewable basis. The Chilworth inventory makes a distinction between common charcoal, which would have been made from alder

Figure 22   Breaking up gunpowder for pressing in the screw press (right). The hard sheets of press cake are then broken up and placed in the sieves of the corning machine behind the curtains on the left (see figure 23).

and willow, and the superior 'dogwood' charcoal. Gunpowder maker's dogwood was alder buckthorn, and it was preferred for fine sporting powder. Sulphur too seems to have been brought in already prepared by specialist sulphur refiners. Most of the saltpetre used in the industry by this time was imported by the East India Company, but powdermakers recycled the waste from the refinery by pouring it on beds of earth, from which saltpetre could be recovered. The valuation shows that this saltpetre earth was a considerable asset.

The inventory lists and values the equipment used in refining the saltpetre and mixing the ingredients. At Chilworth there were four 'stone mills', that is edge-runner incorporating mills, each with one waterwheel. There were nine sets of bedstones and edge runners, that is 27 stones, between them. Edge-runner mills were typically arranged in pairs, one on either side of a waterwheel, but one of those at Chilworth was a double mill, with two on each side, and one, the 'little stone mill', was a single unit.

The next processes are illustrated in figures 22–25.[5] The inventory lists presses (figure 22), to compact the gunpowder before it was corned, and corning machines for forming it into grains (figures 22 and 23). These consisted of double sieves on a shaking frame, operated by a crank which was geared to a waterwheel. There was a glazing tub for tumbling the powder to polish the grains; there were 'hand engines', probably cylindrical gauze-covered screens, for

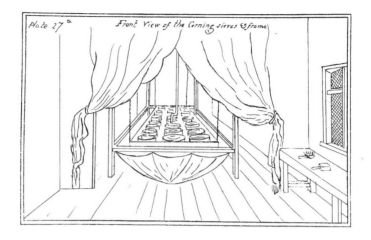

Figure 23 Gunpowder corning or granulating machine, consisting of double sieves on a shaking frame. Blocks of lignum vitae in the sieves break up the press cake and force it through the holes in the upper sieve to be collected in the lower.

separating the grains of powder from loose dust (figure 24) and trays in which the powder was spread out to dry in a stove before it was packed for dispatch to the magazines. The stove would have been of the type known as a 'gloom stove'. It had tiers of shelves for the trays of gunpowder and was heated by the back of an iron fireplace which projected into the room and was stoked from outside (figure 25).

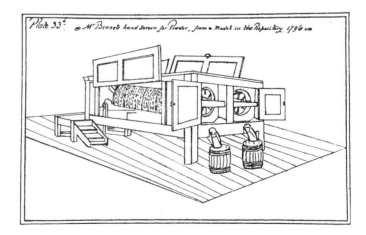

Figure 24 Gunpowder dusting reel. Corned powder is tumbled in the reel and loose dust passes through the mesh of the silk covering.

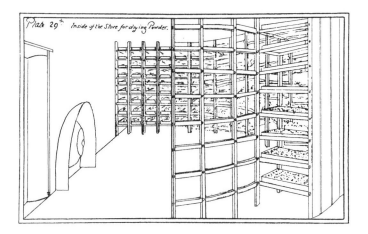

Figure 25 Interior of a gloom stove for drying gunpowder. The room is heated by the back of a fireplace stoked in an adjoining room on the left.

A very large number of barrels was needed both for packing and for use as containers during manufacture but there is no mention in the inventories of a cooperage, except for a small one at the Barking magazine, so barrels were probably bought from specialist coopers in London. Besides the cooper's shop, the stock of powder it held and a skiff, the magazine at Barking had a dwelling house with a garden and brewhouse.

The London office was at Castle Alley, Cornhill. In the office itself there was a mahogany double desk and book case, chairs with black leather seats and 18 ship prints on the wall. There were numerous small items including a tin box 'with 16 sample boxes within the side for the several sorts of gunpowder', a leaden ink stand, a pounce box, sand box, a red ink glass, weights and scales for weighing money, files, a plan of London and a guide to tradesmen. There was also a parlour, dining room, bed chamber, kitchen, cellar, and garrets. In the dining room there was a large blue and white Delft punch bowl and four purple and white coffee cups. The parlour had a mahogany desk and tea table, chairs of Virginia walnut tree with black leather seats, a painted floor cloth (half worn) and two paintings, one of which was a portrait of the Duke of Cumberland. Perhaps this, and the floorcloth, dated from Pearse's previous partnership agreement of 1746, the year the Jacobite cause was defeated at Culloden.

Government factories

During the Seven Years War of 1756–63 the government had great difficulty obtaining enough gunpowder of the required quality, partly because gunpowder technology was not yet based on scientific principles and partly because the powdermakers liked to sell to private customers. The government decided to run its own factories and in 1759 acquired the Faversham mills, followed by Waltham Abbey in 1789 and Ballincollig in County Cork in 1805. The Faversham mills were sold to the Crown by Thomas Pearse's partner Benjamin Pryce, in a manner which was afterwards denounced by the other parties concerned. Chilworth's link with Faversham had thus ended. Benjamin then became superintendent at Faversham and, Thomas Pearse being in financial difficulties, the Chilworth works were run by one Edward Pryce, whose relationship to Benjamin is not clear.[6]

Explosions

Several explosions at the powdermills were recorded in the eighteenth century and in 1727 the corn mill in Albury Park burnt down after an explosion of gunpowder which was being stored there.[7] The corning house explosion in 1760 or 1761 which, as related in chapter 7, killed Gad and Collis at the paper mill and damaged the fabric of the building, was said also to have caused the collapse of St Martha's church half a mile away. The church was shown in a ruined state in a sketch made in 1763[8] and another drawing by 'A Lady', published in the 1830s and reproduced in figure 26, shows it in a similar condition. How far the explosion was responsible for the damage is uncertain. Buildings at a distance from an explosion could indeed be damaged by underground shock waves but the building was probably dilapidated already, as many churches were in the eighteenth century — it was not until the mid-nineteenth century that a great spurt of church building and repair began and St Martha's was not restored until 1848–50.[9]

In 1778 three workers were killed in the corning house at the powder mills. A contemporary report named them as Worsfield, Comber and Charlton but they were remembered in a court case of 1817 as George Walford, Isaac Cumber and Charrington.[10] This explosion was said to have hurled a wheel and a heavy beam a great distance, to have damaged the church further and broken the windows in the manor house.

Figure 26 St Martha's Church, by A Lady, early nineteenth century. Courtesy of Albury History Society.

* * *

The proprietor by this time was Isaac Dent, who had joined Edward Pryce in partnership in 1766 and by 1770 was operating alone. He came from Nettlepot, a remote hamlet which was then in north Yorkshire but is now in County Durham, near Barnard Castle. Whether he became involved in the gunpowder industry through the need for powder in his local lead mines or through more adventurous pursuits is not known. His background presents a difficult challenge to family historians because Dent is a common surname in his native district. He appears to have had some interest in the powder mills at Faversham which had been sold to the government by Benjamin Pryce. At Chilworth he held only yearly tenancies and repeatedly tried to obtain a longer lease from Earl Spencer. Eventually a draft indenture was drawn up for a 36-year lease from Christmas 1789 but in February 1790 Isaac Dent died and left the business to his manager William Tinkler.

The Tinkler Letter Book

Copies of all the letters sent from William Tinkler's London office during the first year of his ownership of the business have survived in the foolscap book in which they were drafted. No doubt similar books existed for subsequent years and were thrown away, but someone saw fit to keep the first one and it provides invaluable insights into the day-to-day working of a powder mill at the end of the eighteenth century.[11]

A typical letter to a customer reads as follows:

Mr Allpress Ashton   London, March 25th 1790
Sir. I am favoured with yours of the 20th inst and above you have bill of parcels of the barrel powder ordered which was delivered yesterday to Fussey's waggon. I am sorry to inform you that Mr Dent is dead. He has left me the gunpowder mills. Shall be very much obliged to you for your favours and will take care to supply you with powder of the same quality as you have been used to have.   WT

The book contains 279 letters, most of which are to customers but 55 are about the management of the business, and 18 deal with Isaac Dent's estate, of which Tinkler was executor. Many of these concern Dent's relatives at Nettlepot.

The gunpowder industry was still mainly concentrated in southeast England, though there were also mills near Bristol and in the Lake District, and Tinkler supplied customers all over the country, together with a few overseas. Customers' addresses are not given but an idea of where they lived can often be deduced from the names of the carriers who delivered their orders, who went to regular destinations.

Many customers were individuals buying powder for shooting and ordering small quantities, typically an eighth or a quarter of a barrel. These small orders were sent by waggon from the inns in London from which the carriers operated. Other customers were dealers or mine owners, who typically bought 8 or 10 barrels at a time but occasionally 20 or 30. One regular customer was a mine owner called Josias Blakeway, whose consignments went from London by Powell's waggon. London directories show that this went to Shrewsbury. There were only two customers in Scotland and both of these were dealers, Messrs David Steuart and Mr Robert Allan. Their orders went by ship to seventeen different ports, including Leith and Saltcoats, and David Steuart arranged one shipment of 100 barrels to a customer in Gibraltar. The other overseas customers were at Limerick in Ireland and in New York.

Most of the letters about running the mills were to Thomas Harri-

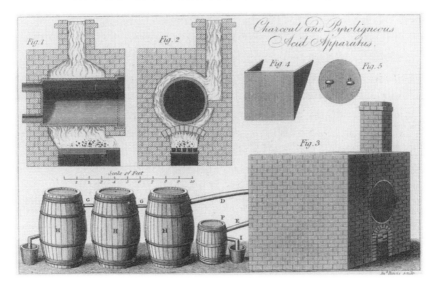

Figure 27 Charcoal cylinders from Parkes's *Chemical Essays*, 1815. Tar and pyroligneous acid are collected in the barrels, leaving an evenly charred product with impurities removed.

son, the manager at Chilworth. Many are about carrying out repairs because Isaac Dent had not been willing to spend a great deal of money on buildings and equipment while he was unable to obtain a long-term lease. Some concern detailed technical matters, two of which are of particular interest.

On 9 August 1790 Tinkler wrote: 'I am informed that the Colliers for the Duke of Richmond has a new way of burning their Coal for Powder desire you will take some proper opportunity to try to find it out.' The Duke of Richmond was Master General of the Ordnance. Major William Congreve at the Royal Laboratory had engaged William Watson, professor of chemistry at Cambridge and Bishop of Llandaff, to devise a way of improving the quality of charcoal by making it more pure and consistent. His method, which was being adopted in the government factories, was to heat the wood in sealed cylindrical retorts from which the impurities were removed, as shown in figure 27.

Another letter shows that saltpetre earth was still being used to recycle the waste liquor from the refinery. On 11 October Tinkler wrote: 'Let the Petre Earth be turned as soon as you can spare the men to do it.' Other letters refer to the East India Company's sale of imported saltpetre which was held twice a year, in March and

September. After the sale the powdermakers met to agree on the price of gunpowder and the powdermakers in the Lake District, where mills had been established near Kendal in 1763, were concerned about being undersold in Scotland.

Many of the letters concern barge transport between London and Guildford, bringing raw materials and other goods to the mills and taking the finished gunpowder to the magazine at Barking Creek. The barges were operated by James Wilkins and John Wilkins of Guildford and used the Thames and the Wey Navigation. Tinkler had a warehouse at Dapdune Wharf, 1 km downstream from Guildford bridge, where the barges were loaded and unloaded. Carts were used to transport materials some 6 km by level road between this wharf and the mills.

Although the Godalming Navigation between Guildford and Godalming was opened in 1763, and this included Stonebridge Wharf at Shalford, only 4 km from the mills, the gunpowder makers continued to use Dapdune Wharf, probably to avoid paying two sets of tolls as the two parts of the navigation were separately run. Indeed Tinkler was brought before a Session of the Peace at Guildford in 1793 for carrying powder through the streets of the town. He protested that this was not unlawful, that it had been done for many years and that people created more danger with fireworks, but said he had directed it to be sent a different way in future.[12]

The Liverpool magazine which appeared in the 1753 inventory is not mentioned in the Tinkler letter book. It therefore seems that the firm had ceased trading at Liverpool by 1790, although several other powdermakers in South-East England, those manufacturing at Ewell, Bedfont, Hounslow and Dartford, are recorded there between 1800 and 1807.[13]

Notes

1. NRO, SOX 488, abstract of lease 1766. This chapter is largely a summary of background information on Chilworth in *Gunpowder Mills: Documents*.
2. Fairclough, K R, 'Thomas Coram: his Brief Period as a Gunpowder Producer', *SyAC*, vol. 86 (1999), 53–72, microfiche 43–92.
3. Morris, Robert Hunter, 'An American in London, 1735–1736: the diary of Robert Hunter Morris', edited by Beverley McAnear, *Pennsylvania Magazine of History and Biography*, vol. 64 (1940), 164–217, 356–406.
4. *Gunpowder Mills: Documents*, Chapter 5: Inventory of Thomas Pearse & Co., 1753.
5. The drawings in figures 22–25 are from an instruction manual of 1796–8 from which copies were made by students. They are based on a notebook in the authors' pos-

session and another version in the Kent Archives Office (U269 0187/1).

6. West, Jenny, *Gunpowder, Government and War in the Mid-Eighteenth Century* (Royal Historical Society, The Boydell Press, 1991).

7. Simmons Collection, quoting *Ipswich Journal*.

8. *VCH*, vol.3, 106; Grose, Francis, *The Antiquities of England* (1773), vol.3, unpaginated.

9. Nairn, I & Pevsner, N, Surrey (Penguin, The Buildings of England, 1962), 135.

10. *Sussex Weekly Advertiser*, 26 October 1778; see also chapter 10.

11. *Gunpowder Mills: Documents*, Chapter 6: The Letter Book of William Tinkler, 1790–1791.

12. SHC: Letter from William Tinkler to Thomas Sibthorpe, 25 October 1793 (BR/QS/5/33(9)).

13. Palmer, A, *The Low Wood Gunpowder Company* (GMSG, 1998), 38. The Low Wood gunpowder site is in Cumbria.

9

The Ball Family of Papermakers, 1790–1824

Charles Ball, who with Captain Wilcocks took over Chilworth paper mills after Joseph Callow became bankrupt in 1791, came from a Northamptonshire family. His father Charles had been paper-maker at Rush Mill, Northampton, from 1763 and he himself moved to Surrey in 1790 and spent a short time at Stoke Mill before going to Chilworth. He dissolved his partnership with Captain Wilcox in 1793 and moved to a mill near the church in the old village of Albury, of which he had taken a 21-year lease.[1]

Originally Albury mill had been a corn mill and is shown as such on the 1782 estate map by Thomas Wedge, on which the sketch map in figure 28 is based.[2] This shows the manor house facing the symmetrical terraced gardens, 400 yards long. The gardens were laid out in 1667 by John Evelyn for Henry Howard, later sixth Duke of Norfolk.[3] They included a vineyard and a yew hedge, again 400 yards long, and a tunnel leading away to the north. There was also a canal taking water from the Tillingbourne and a semi-circular basin with a fountain, fed by a specially constructed leat from Silent Pool, 800 metres to the north-west.[4] William Cobbett in his *Rural Rides* wrote with tremendous enthusiasm about these gardens, particularly the yew hedge, and pronounced them to be the prettiest he had seen.[5] The mill was immediately downstream from the gardens.

Charles Ball converted the corn mill for the manufacture of banknote paper and soon received some orders which provide a fascinating insight into an important aspect of European history. The curious story was told by his grandson, Charles Ashby Ball, as follows:

On a spring day in the year 1793 or 1794, a stranger presented himself at the little mill and, showing my grandsire a blank note with certain

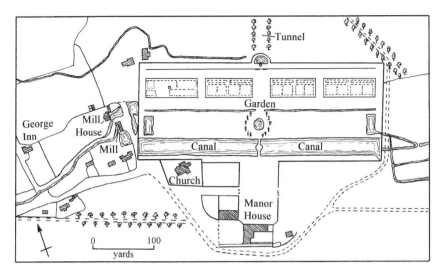

Figure 28   Sketch map based on a detail of a survey of Albury Park in 1782 by Thomas Wedge. The mill and mill house are at the west end of the formal gardens laid out by John Evelyn.

water-marks, inquired if he could undertake a quantity of exactly similar paper. The bargain was concluded on the spot and a time for delivery agreed upon. The stranger was asked to leave his address but he replied that as he was continually travelling he would return at the period agreed upon to receive his paper, and he departed, leaving a heavy sum as deposit. A few days after the expiration of the stipulated time he returned in a post-chaise and, being satisfied with the perfect imitation of the water-mark, he had the paper placed in his carriage, with which he departed, leaving another similar order. These transactions were several times renewed, until on one occasion the unknown required for a new order various changes to be made in the water-marks. The 'former' or 'form-maker' of the mill was sent for. He was a young man named Longhelt, a native of Germany, with whom I remember to have talked in my youth. The stranger explained to him the alteration he wanted to be made, and sat down by his side for the purpose of seeing him begin his labor. Longhelt who had been drinking, resented the intrusion, and getting impatient at the stranger's interventions, he waxed furious and threw the form at the visitor's head. The latter went to complain to my grandfather, who advised his customer not to attempt the supervision till the morrow, when the modifications were successfully made. Further alterations to the form were continually being made, but after some time the stranger departed to be seen no more.

Some time after this my grandfather learned that his mysterious patron was no other than the Comte d'Artois, afterwards Charles X, king of France and Navarre, and that the note paper he had manufactured was for the purpose of being converted into false assignats, with which France

Figure 29 An *assignat* for 125 livres issued on the 7th day of the first month of the second year of the French Revolutionary calendar (12 October 1796). Note that counterfeiters were to be punished by death. Courtesy of Tony de Reuck.

was at that time inundated. The frequent changes of the water-mark are accounted for from the fact that when the officers of the Republic discovered the forgeries, they altered the form of the assignats. So soon as they appeared, copies were at once forwarded to the Comte d'Artois in England whence he procured copies.

I may add that on one occasion my grandfather finding that he was manufacturing Russian bank-note paper, gave up the forms to the Prince of Lieven then Ambassador to England, and the Emperor of Russia presented him with £500 to indemnify him for the loss of his order.[6]

Hence Charles Ball played a role in the attempt of the French royal family to undermine the Revolution by forging *assignats*. These were a form of paper currency issued by the French Republic from 1789 to 1797 and then abandoned as the public refused to accept them because they were worthless. An example of an *assignat* is shown in figure 29. Many French emigrés who had fled to England during the Revolution took up residence in Surrey, particularly around Dorking, and the Comte d'Artois is said to have lived at Shalford Rectory Manor during his exile.[7]

Charles Ball paid the land tax for Albury Park Mill until 1810.[8] For much of this period he was the tax assessor and kept the records in booklets made from his own paper. Two watermarks copied from this paper are shown in figure 30. One of these is an elaborate PRO

Figure 30 Tracings of watermarks of the Ball family, including Charles Ball senior (Pro Patria and 1799), Charles Ball junior (B 1816, 1812, 1819) and Edmund Richard Ball (1811, 1816; with Wm Ashby, 1818).

PATRIA design based on a Dutch original in which the Maid of Holland protects, with the help of a lion, the boundaries of her country, symbolically represented by a fence. Ball was presumably indicating that his paper was as good as imported paper, rather than pretending that it was made in Holland.

This was a period when many master papermakers were having problems with their workers and Ball was active in meetings of the

employers. For example with other local papermakers he was a sig-
natory to a letter warning the men not to assist journeymen who
were striking for higher wages.[9]

Mr. Davis Sir
In consequence of what passed at the meeting of the Master Papermakers
at the George and Vulture on Tuesday last, We of that Branch in the
Neighbourhood have had a meeting when it was unanimously agreed to
give our Men a fortnights warning from this day, unless they comply
with all the terms required and agreed to at the Second Meeting namely
'to desist from giving any assistance to those Men who have continued
against their Masters for an advance of Wages' and also 'to desist from
what is called their Turns to the Journeymen at present out of work' till
they return to their Duty. We hope these measures may prove efficacious
and beg of you to lay these our resolutions before the Committee.
We remain Sir
Your humble Servants
Edward Hughs, Chas Ball, Smith & Knight, John Groves, Thomas Harrison, Guildford, March 26, 1796

At this time Hughes was at Chilworth Mills, Ball at Albury Park,
Smith and Knight at Westbrook Mill, Godalming, Groves at Stoke
Mill, Guildford, and Harrison at Catteshall Mill, Godalming. How-
ever attendance at meetings appears to have been a burden and in
1799 Ball and Hughes represented each other and on one occasion
Ball also represented Richard Glover of Morden paper mill on the
River Wandle in what is now south-west London.[10]
The print of 'Albury Mill & Paper Mould Manufactory near
Guildford in Surry' reproduced in figure 31, represents Albury Park
Mill in about 1800.[11] The relative locations of the mill house, the
paper mill itself and the watercourses correspond well with those in
the 1782 survey shown in figure 28. The print, which was engraved
by Ashby, is taken from a letterhead and the original measures only
56 millimetres across. It shows an overshot clasped-arm waterwheel,
typical of the period, and large shuttered drying lofts. The fact that
the mill made moulds is consistent with the manufacture of banknote paper in general and the above *assignat* story in particular.
Indeed Harry Ashby, a London printer and engraver specialising in
bill-heads, banknotes and specimen sheets of calligraphy, was a business partner of Charles Ball.[12] There also appears to have been a
family connection, as Charles Ashby Ball was born at Albury in

Figure 31 Engraving of Albury Park Mill at the beginning of the nineteenth century, enlarged from a letterhead measuring 56mm across. The shuttered drying lofts, single-storey workshops and clasped-arm waterwheel are characteristic. Courtesy of Guildford Museum.

1809,[13] and William May Ashby and Edmund Richard Ball took out a new lease of Postford Upper Mill in 1815.[14]

Prior to the arrival of Charles Ball at Albury Park Mill, the manor was held by Admiral William Clement Finch who harassed the Albury villagers living near the church and manor house so much that many of them moved to the nearby hamlet of Weston Street shown on figure 1. Finch died in 1794 and during Ball's occupation of the paper mill the village remained stable. In particular from 1800 to 1810 the manor was occupied by Samuel Thornton, a governor of the Bank of England, who was a public-spirited landlord.[15] However, there is no evidence that Ball produced paper for the Bank of England.

In 1809 Charles Ball of Albury Park Mill took out leases of 61 years on two newly-constructed paper mills at Postford, 2.5 km down the valley from Albury Park, on the parish boundary between Albury and St Martha's.[16] He installed his sons Charles and Edmund Richard there and he himself retired in 1810. He built Post Ford Hill, the residence shown in figure 32, which is now known as

Figure 32 Post Ford Hill [Postford House], by A Lady, probably about 1820. The view is from the south-east as indicated by the plan of the house shown on the map of figure 34. Courtesy of Albury History Society.

Postford House, and probably lived there, although he died in London in 1820 and is buried in St John's churchyard at Merrow. His obituary stated that he was 'eminent as the inventor and manufacturer of superior bankers' note paper, and late of the firm of Ball and Ashby, engravers etc'.[17]

The two new mills were on the site of the Upper gunpowder works which had been vacated when Sir Polycarpus Wharton left at the end of the seventeenth century and were shown with the ponds empty on the Chilworth estate map of 1728. There are no records of industrial activity at Postford in the eighteenth century and the ponds are labelled 'fish ponds' on a survey of Albury Glebe lands dated 1803.[18] The upper pond, which is now known as Waterloo Pond but was earlier called Pens or Payne's Pond, is fed by springs and the water of the Tillingbourne bypasses it by means of a leat to enter the large lower pond. This also receives water from the Postford or Law Brook and is known as Postford Great Pond or simply Postford Pond. However, collectively the names Albury Ponds or Chilworth Ponds are also used. It is not surprising therefore that several different names are also used for the mills on the site. In particular, the twentieth century corn mill was known as Albury Mill as the owners, the Botting family, previously worked the mill at the centre

Figure 33　Postford Lower Mill, by A Lady, probably about 1820. The view is from the south-west and shows the mill pond in the centre foreground, the old road from Chilworth to Albury, which follows the mill dam, and the mill building, consisting almost entirely of drying lofts. Courtesy of Albury History Society.

of modern Albury and brought its name to Postford when they moved there in 1909. The mills where Charles Ball the younger and Edmund Richard Ball were established in 1809 will here be called Postford Lower and Postford Upper Mills respectively. A contemporary drawing of the Lower Mill is reproduced in figure 33.

When the Chilworth Manor estates were sold in 1813 the two Postford mills were described as newly erected and each had three vats. A detail of the accompanying plan is reproduced as figure 34. It has 'Paper Mills' labelled at the north end of the half of Albury or Postford Pond which was included in the Manor but does not show explicitly the Upper Mill at Payne's Pond. Lidwell, which provided spring water to the mills, is marked and there are hop gardens along the valley floor. The adjacent property of Albury Glebe is also indicated. The schedule states that the Lower Mill had an overshot waterwheel 11 feet in diameter and 11 feet wide and was used to make banknote paper. The Upper Mill had an overshot wheel 11 feet in diameter and 5 feet wide. The combined annual rent was £168.[19]

In the first available excise lists of 1816 the Upper and Lower Mills were allocated numbers 386 and 387 and were held by Ball

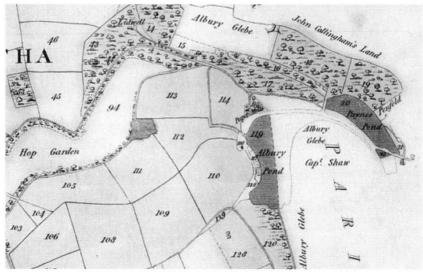

Copyright of Surrey History Service.

Figure 34   Detail of estate map from the sale particulars of Chilworth Manor, 1813. Postford Lower Mill is shown as 'Paper Mills' at Albury (Postford) Pond. Postford Upper Mill, which was at Paynes Pond, is not marked although it is listed in the printed schedule under plot 17. Post Ford Hill (figure 32) is shown but not named in plot 128. Reproduced by permission of the Surrey History Service (G85/2/1(2) no. 4).

and Ashby and by Charles Ball junior.[20] The watermarks 'ERB 1811', 'E BALL & W ASHBY 1816', 'C BALL JUNR 1812', 'B 1816' and 'C BALL 1819' shown in figure 30 are consistent with this information. The link between the Ball and Ashby families has been noted above; in particular William May Ashby and Edmund Richard Ball appear to have taken on a new lease of the Upper Mill on Christmas Day 1815.[21]

A visit to the mills at about this time was later recalled by the author Martin Tupper (1810–1889):

A banknote experience: when a very small child I used to be taken to the Postford paper-mill at Albury . . . I was deputed to amuse myself by making banknote paper, as thus: a spoonful of pulp put into a shallow tray of wire and shaken deftly made a small oblong of paper duly impressed with Britannia and water-marked: being then dried on a flannel pad. Many years after, when I was preparing for Oxford under Mr. Holt at Postford House, there was discovered a secret cupboard in the wall of his drawing-room which was found to contain several forged plates for printing banknotes: and this discovery accounted for the recent suicide of a Mr. H—, a previous owner of the paper-mill, who evidently feared exposure and conviction.[22]

The banks for which banknote paper was made at Postford included the Bank of Ireland, the British Linen Bank, the Royal Bank, the Aberdeen Bank and the Perth Bank. Charles Ball clearly felt that he was producing paper of high quality as in 1818 he submitted a sample to the Bank of England, though without success.[23] Following the Napoleonic Wars many banks failed so that banknote papermakers were in difficulties. In 1820 Edmund Ball and William Ashby became bankrupt and the Upper Mill, described as a banknote paper mill, was for sale by auction (figure 35). An advertisement in *The Times* states that about 1,000 reams of banknote paper suitable for the Irish, Dundee, Isle of Wight and other banks would be auctioned, together with 115 reams suitable for Irish Linens.[24]

The mill was taken over by Hugh Rowland of Chilworth Mills but Charles Francis Hayes and John Hayes were there in 1824. One wonders whether one of them could have been the Mr H— mentioned by Martin Tupper or whether Tupper invented the whole story. In 1826 the Hayes, together with a Charles M'Callum, were bankrupt. Meanwhile, at the Lower Mill, Charles Ball was bankrupt in 1821 and the mill, now with four vats, and the residence of Post Ford Hill were for sale. Ball was joined by Charles Roffe and a year later they were also operating at Stoke Mill in Guildford. In 1824 Roffe became the sole proprietor but he too was bankrupt a year later.[25] Ball & Roffe watermarks dated 1821 and 1823 have been recorded.[26]

In practice Charles Ball and his young son Charles Ashby emigrated to France and in 1826 became partners in the firm of Gosse, Ball and Muller at a new paper mill at Gueures, near Dieppe. This had been established by the Comte de Tocqueville, an anglophile who had spent time and married in England and was following English practice in bringing industry to his local village. The partnership started another paper mill nearby at Val Vernier in 1840 and the Balls continued working in the district until 1860. Charles Ashby Ball also bought paper mills at Doullens in Picardie in 1836 and at Pont Audemer near le Havre in 1844. His son, Allen Charles Ball, was papermaker at Pont Audemer in the 1860s.[27]

Charles Ashby Ball perfected many important improvements in the manufacture of paper, especially in the use of esparto grass and

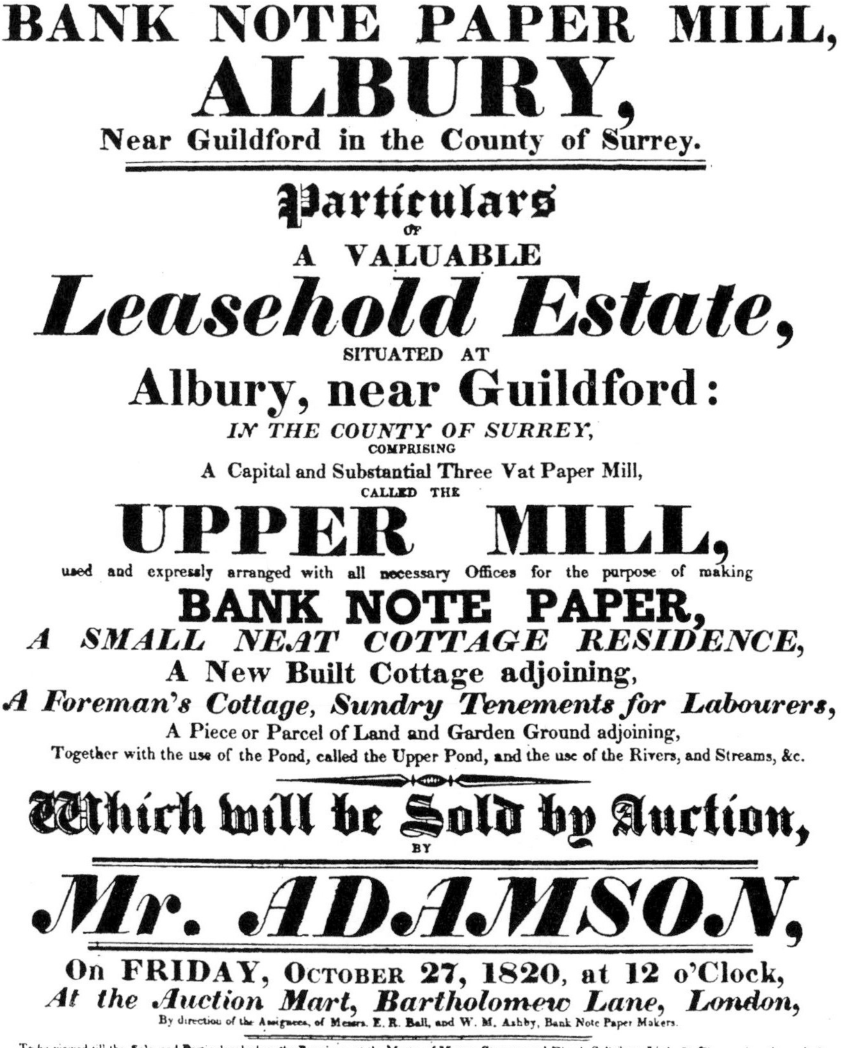

BANK NOTE PAPER MILL,

ALBURY,

Near Guildford in the County of Surrey.

Particulars

OF

A VALUABLE

Leasehold Estate,

SITUATED AT

Albury, near Guildford:

IN THE COUNTY OF SURREY,

COMPRISING

A Capital and Substantial Three Vat Paper Mill,

CALLED THE

UPPER MILL,

used and expressly arranged with all necessary Offices for the purpose of making

BANK NOTE PAPER,

A SMALL NEAT COTTAGE RESIDENCE,

A New Built Cottage adjoining,

A Foreman's Cottage, Sundry Tenements for Labourers,

A Piece or Parcel of Land and Garden Ground adjoining,

Together with the use of the Pond, called the Upper Pond, and the use of the Rivers, and Streams, &c.

Which will be Sold by Auction,

BY

Mr. ADAMSON,

On FRIDAY, OCTOBER 27, 1820, at 12 o'Clock,

At the Auction Mart, Bartholomew Lane, London,

By direction of the Assignees, of Messrs. E. R. Ball, and W. M. Ashby, Bank Note Paper Makers.

To be viewed till the Sale, and Particulars had on the Premises; at the Mart; of Messrs. Stevens and Wood, Solicitors, Little St. Thomas Apostle; and of
Mr ADAMSON, 88, Fenchurch Street.

Copyright of Surrey History Service.

Figure 35   Poster advertising the sale of Postford Upper Mill in October 1820.
Reproduced by permission of the Surrey History Service (G85/2/1(1) no. 141).

bleached straw as raw material. He died near le Havre in 1885.[28]
One wonders whether his grandfather's link with Charles X of
France helped in his successful career.

Notes

1. Crocker, A & Phillips, A, 'The Ball Family, Papermakers of Surrey and Northern France', in *IPH Congressbook* vol.9 (Vienna, 1992), 52–62.
2. SyAS Library, Survey of Finch Estates at Albury by Thomas Wedge, 1782 (M14/ALB/4).
3. Brandon, P, *A History of Surrey* (Phillimore, 1977), 63–6.
4. Walmsley, R C, *The Risbridger Story* (Albury, Old Parish Church [c.1976]).
5. Cobbett, W, *Rural Rides*, 1830 (rep. Penguin, 1967), 98–9.
6. *The Stationer and Fancy Trades' Register*, 5 April 1869, 196.
7. Rambles Round Guildford (Guildford, Lasham, [c.1890]), 113.
8. SHC, Land tax (QS6/7, Albury).
9. SHC, Letter of 26 March 1796 on reverse of MS index to Russell's *History of Guildford* (SP 942 21, GU1).
10. Shorter, *Paper Mills*, 236; Crocker, A, 'The Paper Mills of Surrey, part 2', *Surrey History*, vol.4 no.4 (1992), 211–230, at pp.219–20.
11. Guildford Museum, TG 1099.
12. Maxted, I, *The London Book Trades, 1775–1800* (Dawson, 1977).
13. Boase, F, *Modern English Biography*, vol.1 (Cass, 1965), 145.
14. Simmons Collection.
15. Walmsley, R C, *Albury Park* (Albury, 1974); Walmsley, R C, *Drummond's Chapel* (Albury, [c.1980]); Manning & Bray, vol.2, 125.
16. SHC, Chilworth estate sale particulars, 1813 (G85/2/1(2), no.4).
17. *Gentleman's Magazine*, 90(1), 1820, 284.
18. SyAS Library, Copy of survey of Albury Glebe, 1803 (M14/ALB/5).
19. SHC, Sale particulars 1813.
20. Simmons Collection.
21. *The Times*, 18 Oct. 1820, 4e.
22. Tupper, M F, *My Life as an Author* (Sampson Low, 1886), 334–5.
23. Crocker & Phillips (see note 1), 56.
24. Simmons Collection; SHC, Sale poster of Postford Upper Mill, 1820 (G85/2/1(1), no.141); *The Times*, 21 June 1820, 4e and 18 Oct. 1820, 4e.
25. Simmons Collection; SHC, Land tax; SHC, Sale particulars of Postford Hill House, 1821 (G85/2/1(2) no.24/2).
26. Crocker, A, 'Surrey Watermarks', *The Quarterly*, vol.16 supp. (BAPH, 1995), 4; Crocker, A, 'The Paper Mills of Surrey', *Surrey History*, vol.4 no.1 (1989–90), 61.
27. Crocker & Phillips (see note 1).
28. Boase, see note 13.

10

Chilworth Mills: Paper Versus Gunpowder

From 1803 to 1835 Chilworth Great and Little Paper Mills were worked by Hugh Rowland and his son of the same name. Until 1819 Rowland was in partnership with Hugh Crowder[1] who was also his partner for a few years at Westbrook Mill, Godalming. They were soon in dispute with William Tinkler, the gunpowder maker at Chilworth, over the use of water, a common cause of conflict between the proprietors of mills. Tinkler used a particular stream, which came from the system for flowing the meadows, for soaking the saltpetre earth, and the papermakers had diverted it into the mill pond to provide more power for their waterwheels. The matter was resolved by an agreement drawn up in 1805 that the papermakers would make a ditch to divert the water back to the saltpetre earth. Figure 36 is based on a detail of an accompanying map. The complete map also shows the extensive channels and sluices for flowing the meadows and gives details of the sequence of their operation.[2]

Meanwhile Chilworth Manor had changed hands. The Earl Spencer had sold the estate in 1796 to Edmund Hill, a powdermaker of Hounslow, who had plans to expand the works and applied for permission to build another powder mill. This was refused because the new mill would have been within half a mile of St Martha's Church, which would have contravened an Act of Parliament of 1772.[3] Edmund Hill was in poor health and his business was taken over by John Fish, who put the Chilworth estate up for sale again in 1813.[4]

William Tinkler's business was prospering at this time. No doubt he lost much of his trade in Scotland when gunpowder mills were established near Edinburgh in 1794 and 1805,[5] but this must have been compensated for by the demand for powder for the French

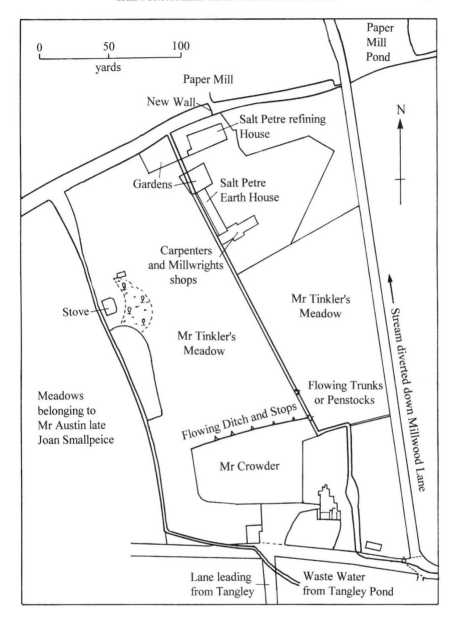

Figure 36 Disputed water channels, 1805. Redrawn from a map accompanying the articles of agreement between Tinkler and Crowder & Rowland (SHC: G1/47/ 3/2a). The papermakers had diverted the channel serving the saltpetre refinery down Millwood Lane and into the mill pond.

Revolutionary Wars, which started in 1793, and the Napoleonic Wars which followed. At the 1813 sale, he purchased the manor.[6]

The paper mills in 1813

The mills are shown on the detail of the 1813 estate map reproduced in figure 37. The Great Paper Mill had a breast-shot waterwheel 17 feet (5.2m) in diameter and 8 feet wide, two vats, two beating engines, drying lofts over the mill, sizing, rag and cart houses and a stable. The Little Paper Mill had an overshot waterwheel 17 feet in diameter and 7 feet wide, two vats, two beating engines, a sol and drying lofts. The buildings were either brick and tiled or boarded and tiled and the combined annual rent was £150. Since 1763 the number of waterwheels had been reduced from five to two.[7]

In 1813 Rowland sought the advice of the engineer Bryan Donkin, who had just developed the first successful paper-making machine, about the proximity of gunpowder 'danger buildings' to his mills, but no conclusion appears to have been reached. His contact with Donkin does not seem to have resulted in him acquiring a machine

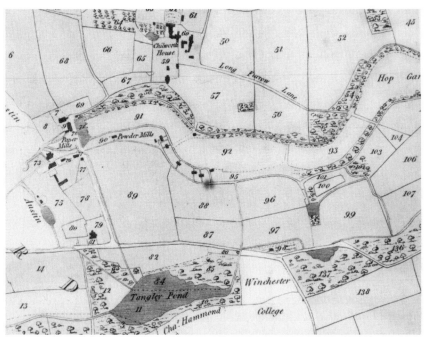

Copyright of Surrey History Service.

Figure 37   Detail of estate map from the sale particulars of Chilworth Manor, 1813. William Tinkler holds the powder mills (90 and 95), the dwelling house (79) and several plots of land including dogwood (alder buckthorn) coppices for charcoal (14 and 15 on figure 34). Crowder and Rowland hold the paper mills (72 and 73) the dam (71), the house adjoining the powder mill house (81) and several other plots. Numbers 91–95 and 100 are hop grounds. Reproduced by permission of the Surrey History Service (G85/2/1(2) no. 4).

Figure 38 Watermarks of Hugh Rowland and a post-horn watermark of James Simmons of Haslemere. The latter reproduces the complete device of which a detail of the wire construction is shown in figure 16.

however as hand-made paper made by him has been discovered with the watermark 1822 (figure 38).[8]

The gunpowder mills in 1813

At the west end of the site in 1813, in addition to the stove, earth house, boiling house and workshops which had been there in 1728, there was now a cylinder house and a shed for refining brimstone. The cylinder house was for making charcoal by the improved method which William Tinkler had heard about in 1790. Tinkler leased dogwood (alder buckthorn) coppices for charcoal near Postford Pond, at the foot of Colyers Hanger (plots 15 and 16 in figure 34). A fifth incorporating mill had evidently been built as in the eastern part of the works there were now five powder mills, each with one water wheel about 24 feet (7.4m) in diameter and 3 feet wide and two pairs of edge-runner stones, a brimstone house, composition house, corning house, dusting house, coal house, watch house etc. with a good stream of water.

Tinkler v Rowland

Further information about the powder mills comes from a detailed account of a court case in 1817.[9] Relations between Rowland and Tinkler had remained strained since the dispute over water in 1805 and deteriorated further when Tinkler became Rowland's landlord. Rowland first instigated a prosecution of the powdermakers at Guildford in 1816. The main charge was that in about 1815 Tinkler had built a dusting house on a site 114 yards (105m) from the paper mill. This site had been occupied by the corning house (G4 in figure 17) which had blown up and damaged the paper mill in 1760 or 1761 and had been replaced by a new corning house on another site farther away. It was further charged that the construction of the new building was unsafe as it was built of brick and stone with a very heavy roof and plastered walls. Danger buildings needed to have a mainly light-weight construction to minimise the damage from any explosion. It was also alleged that more gunpowder was kept on the premises than was allowed by the gunpowder Act of 1772.

On this occasion the matter was settled out of court. Tinkler agreed to pay £400 expenses and to be bound by the directions of an arbitrator who would inspect the works and specify improvements. Major By of the Royal Engineers, who was manager of the government's works at Woolwich and superintendent of the Royal Gunpowder Factory at Waltham Abbey, was appointed arbitrator and his instructions were followed.

In spite of this, a second prosecution was brought at Kingston in April 1817. The proceedings were taken down in shorthand and published in the same year under the title *Chilworth Powder Mills; Trial by an Indictment Charging Them as a Nuisance: by which they were Proved to be not only no Nuisance but as Safe as any, if not the Safest Powder Mills in the Kingdom.*

It is this report which gives the date of 1704 for the conversion of the Lower gunpowder works to paper mills, of which the relevant deeds have since been lost, and which describes the accidents in 1760/1 and 1778. It also shows that local people had long been in the habit of walking through the danger area of the gunpowder works to go to church at St Martha's and that funeral parties had been accustomed to pass within 100 yards of danger buildings. It states that there was no main magazine on the site and finished powder was taken to a magazine at Stoke-next-Guildford, where there was a 'powder house' at Dapdune Wharf.[10]

The report is an invaluable source of information on equipment and working practices in a gunpowder factory in the early nineteenth century. The use of the terms 'dusting house' and 'corning house' in the account of the trial appears confusing because both processes, as well as pressing and glazing, were carried on in the same building. It was 40–50 ft long by 15 ft wide and had two storeys. Pressing and corning (figures 22, 23) were done in the same room, on the upper floor. There were two corning frames with 8 or 12 sieves between them, and they received their shaking motion from a single crank. Two wooden glazing barrels were located in the 'dusting house'. There was much concern about the gloom stove where the powder was dried, as it was considered more dangerous than a steam-heated stove.

Comparison was made with practice at the government factory at Waltham Abbey since William Drayson, the clerk of works there, was giving evidence for the prosecution. We learn that Waltham Abbey had installed drying stoves heated by steam, but that these were a very modern invention and the old gloom stoves were continuing to be used. Dangerous processes were carried out in separate buildings at Waltham Abbey, but this arrangement had only been adopted within the past four years.

For the defence, much was made of the fact of Rowland's grievances. In particular he had been heard to say that 'if Mr Tinkler had but given him a stream of water to his paper-mill, he never would have indicted'. It was also remarked that he had been so little alarmed by the danger that 'not long ago, he went, with his gun, and fired at game, close to the corning house; aye, and dusting-house, which he complains of, by this indictment; and seeks to have removed, on account of its being a building that is dangerous to the neighbourhood in which it stands'. He had also extended the paper mill and built some workers' cottages nearby. This probably refers to the conversion of the drying house of the Little Paper Mill (F8 in figure 17), into the pair of cottages which survives today as Rose Cottage and The Old Cottage.

Major By said that his directions for improvement had been followed since the 1816 prosecution. They included building a protective barrier or 'traverse' to screen Rowland's house from the new danger building and replacing the top part of the brick walls of the new danger building with weather-boarding. The works were now run according to his directions, regarding the construction of the buildings and the quantity of powder handled.

The jury gave a verdict of Not Guilty and Mr Justice Dallas pronounced that 'this is the most malicious prosecution I ever remember brought into a Court of Justice.'

William Tinkler was soon to retire from the business for in 1819 he leased the powder mills to John Sharp. He would then have been aged about 69 for he died in December 1831 at the age of 81.[11] His son, also named William Tinkler, continued to hold the manor until 1845. His inscription 'W.T.1842' can be seen on the downstream side of a bridge facing the old pumphouse on the west side of Blacksmith Lane.

William Cobbett

It was on 30 November 1822 that William Cobbett visited Chilworth and Albury towards the end of the second of his *Rural Rides* and deplored the use of the waters of the Tillingbourne for the manufacture of gunpowder and banknotes. His celebrated diatribe against these inventions is quoted in the frontispiece. He went on to remark that the only redeeming factor in the case of the paper mills was that they had assisted in 'turning rags into Registers'.[12] This was a reference to his independent Radical journal, the *Political Register*, in which he campaigned for political and financial reform. There are no records of banknote paper being made at Chilworth Mills — and it is stressed that banknotes were never actually printed in the valley — so Cobbett must have meant Postford where, at the time of his visit, the Rowlands and Ball & Roffe were working. The paper for the *Registers* could however have been made at Chilworth, where Rowland continued to hold the lease until 1835.

*   *   *

Watermarks of Hugh Rowland are shown in figure 38. In 1816 his two Chilworth mills had excise numbers 388 and 487 but the entries are mysteriously deleted.[13] Rowland also held the nearby Postford Upper Mill from 1821 to 1824. In 1822 he appealed to the Overseer of the Parish of Albury 'against the last poor-rate' and stated that 'I will prove by my Book in a Court of Justice that I derive no profit from the mill but am a loser by it.'[14] Hugh Rowland senior was bankrupt in 1829–30 but his son seems to have continued at Chilworth as four years later mill 388 was working, although 487 was no longer in use.[15] Like the Ball family at Postford, Rowland went in search of better opportunities on the Continent and by 1834 Rowland junior was a paper-maker at Blagny near Abbeville in France.[16] He was bankrupt in 1837 but five years later an English papermaker called Rowland was visited by Bryan Donkin at mills near Heidelberg in Germany.[17]

Notes

1. Simmons Collection; Godalming Museum, Woods Hundred vol. 6, 591.
2. SHC, Articles of agreement in Tinkler v Crowder & Rowland, 1805 (G1/47/3(1) 2a,b)
3. SHC, Quarter Sessions, 6 Oct. 1801 (QS2/1/31).
4. SHC, Sale particulars of Chilworth Estate, 1813 (G85/2/1).
5. *Gazetteer*
6. SHC, Land tax returns (QS6/7, St Martha, 1815).
7. The 17-foot diameter waterwheel at the Great mill had a head of 12ft 6in so that it was high breast-shot. It is therefore surprising that the 17-foot diameter waterwheel at the Little mill was said to be overshot.
8. Clapperton, R H, *The Paper-making Machine. Its Invention, Evolution and Development*, (Oxford, Pergammon, 1967), 74;

Crocker, A, 'Surrey Watermarks', *The Quarterly: Rev. British Assoc. of Paper Historians*, no.16 (Sept. 1995), 1–16; SHC, Albury Parish vouchers 1796–1828, note dated 15 Apr. 1823 (RB 1620).
9. Tinkler, W, *Chilworth Powder Mills; Trial by an Indictment Charging them as a Nuisance* (London, 1817).
10. Shown on a map of 1800 in Clark, L, *Stoke-next-Guildford* (Phillimore, 1999), 18.
11. St Martha's Parish Registers.
12. Cobbett, W, *Rural Rides*, 1830 (rep. Penguin, 1967), 97–100.
13. Simmons Collection.
14. SHC, Albury Parish vouchers 1796–1828, Letter dated 12 August 1822 (RB 1620).
15. Simmons Collection.
16. Simmons Collection.
17. Clapperton (see note 8), 164.

11

Machine-made Paper at Chilworth and Postford

The end of the eighteenth century was a turning point for the paper-making industry. The demand for paper was increasing rapidly as the population became literate and more newspapers were produced. The newly-invented Fourdrinier paper-making machine, which produced continuous rolls of paper rather than individual sheets, speeded up production and steam engines were installed in some mills to supplement water power for driving the beating engines to increase the production of stuff.

Fourdrinier machines were expensive and could only be afforded by the more wealthy mill owners. As a result many of the small mills closed and there were frequent bankruptcies. The skilled workers, who had served seven-year apprenticeships, were concerned about the effect the new equipment would have on their jobs and organised themselves into the Original Society of Papermakers. Likewise the employers set up the Committee of Master Paper-makers, partly to campaign against excise duty on paper, which held back demand. In practice, the total number of people employed in paper making increased rapidly and the main problem was the supply of raw materials. Good quality rags were in short supply but bleaches were discovered which enabled poorer rags to be used. Experiments were also being carried out in the use of alternative raw materials and china clay started to be used to make paper whiter and heavier.[1]

After members of the Ball and Rowland families went to the Continent to improve their prospects, the new proprietors of the paper mills at Chilworth and Postford modernised the works and installed paper-making machines.

Postford Paper Mills

In August 1826 Robert Stephenson & Sons of Newcastle upon Tyne recorded an order from C Magnay & Sons of London for paper-making and other machinery for Postford Mill costing over £600.[2]

The Magnays were a successful family of wholesale stationers and papermakers. Christopher Magnay, who was an alderman of the City of London from 1809 until his death in 1826, held three paper mills in Buckinghamshire in 1816 and also had mills in Norwich and Cork.[3] His sons, William and James, took over Postford Mills and clearly planned to convert them to the production of machine-made paper. However for three years while they made their preparations they installed William Boyd as the papermaker at the Lower Mill. The Upper Mill seems to have been unused after 1826 although it was 1831 before it was recorded as 'discontinued' in the excise records.[4]

In 1832 the Magnays took out a new lease of the mills from William Tinkler, son of the former gunpowder maker at Chilworth and now owner of the Chilworth Manor estates. It gave William and James Magnay authority to 'pull down, take to pieces and sell or convert to their own use the Upper Mill and the water and other wheels, going gears, machinery and other apparatus for the purpose of working the Lower Mill and the other mill to be erected near, and also the use of the stream of water running and flowing from the Luttrell otherwise Ludwell Spring'. Clean spring water from Lid Well, shown north-west of the mill in figure 34, was already being conveyed to the site by pipes and the foundations of the new building had been prepared. This was to be brick and timber with a slate roof and its power supply was to be at least equal to that of the Upper Mill which was being pulled down. The existing insurance cover of £2,000 was to be increased to £3,500 when the buildings were complete.[5]

These developments give rise to further confusion about the names of the mills at Postford. The mill on Waterloo Pond, which has so far been referred to as Postford Upper Mill, was discontinued, yet further references occur to an 'upper mill'. It has been deduced from various pieces of evidence that this was the new mill and that it was situated in the grounds of Postford House, the house which had been built as Post Ford Hill by Charles Ball in 1810. It was now the residence of James Magnay who in practice ran Postford Mill.[6] A building with a waterwheel pit corresponding to contemporary

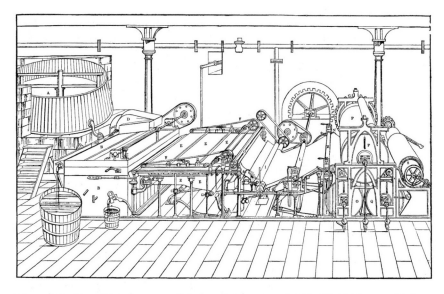

Figure 39   Fourdrinier papermaking machine at Postford Mill, 1833. a: stuff chest
with stirrer and spout; b: vat 5 feet wide and 4 feet long; c: sifter formed of a wire
frame which jumps up and down; d: lifter returning pulp, which drains through the
wire web, to the vat; e: endless web of wire which carries wet paper from the vat
to the felt; f: deckle straps restricting the width of the paper; g: wire cylinder known
as a dandy roll which impresses laid and chain lines on the paper; h: lower roll of
endless wire; i: roller covered with wet felt pressing paper against h; k: first roller
of the endless felt; l, m: first and second pairs of pressing rollers; n: roller receiving
paper at end of felt; o, p, q: large polished drying cylinders heated by steam to
80°F, 100°F and 120°F respectively; r: last felted roller; s: reel. The machine worked
at 25 feet per minute. From the *Penny Magazine,* 1833.

descriptions survives there, near the entrance to the drive of Postford
House in the Dorking Road. It is situated on the leat from the Postford Brook which had served Twist Mill, one of the gunpowder mills
of the Upper Works in the seventeenth century. The 1728 survey of
the Chilworth estate suggests that it was not on precisely the same
site as Twist Mill but was some 60 metres farther downstream. The
Magnays' 'upper' mill will be referred to here as the Postford House
Mill.

In 1833 the works appear to have been in full production. The
Penny Magazine, published by the Society for the Diffusion of Useful
Knowledge, which was printed on paper from Postford, contained a
detailed account of the way in which the paper was produced.[7] The
illustration of papermaking by hand from this article, which is based
on a mill in Kent, is reproduced on the back cover and in figure 14.
The diagrams showing machines at Postford are reproduced as fig-

Figure 40   Cowper paper-cutting machine at Postford Mill, 1833. s (at left): reel from the paper-making machine; t (at top): drum on which the paper is cut into two widths by a circular knife; v (right centre): series of sharp teeth which regularly cut the paper into the required lengths. From the *Penny Magazine*, 1833.

ures 39 and 40. The stuff flows from a chest and vat on to a continuous moving web of wire and thence around a series of drying rollers before being reeled as paper. In practice paper was still needed as individual sheets for both hand-writing and printing and therefore the reels of paper had to be cut. The cutting machine at Postford, operated by two women, is shown in figure 40.

Trade must have been flourishing as in 1833 James Magnay also took over Westbrook Mill in Godalming and in 1838 Stoke Mill north of Guildford. Then in 1842, aged 42, he died following a fall from his horse.[8] His elder brother William, who in 1838 had become, like his father before him, an alderman of the City of London, took over responsibility for the mill. He was Lord Mayor of London in 1843–4 and knighted in 1844.[9] In the late 1840s Sir William Magnay at Albury was said to be the principal papermaker of Surrey, having two papermaking machines and nine beating engines powered by a 12-foot fall of water.[10] During this period the

Figure 41 'Postford Mills near Guildford', by J Weare, *c.*1850. The view is from the south-west. Note the smoking chimney shaft of the Lower Mill and the cottages at the right near the site of the Upper Mill. Courtesy of Guildford Museum.

names of Charles, George and Jane Magnay are also linked to the mill.[11] The lithograph shown as figure 41 probably dates from this time.[12] It illustrates the picturesque setting of the mill looking north-east across Postford Pond. The cluster of cottages to the right are near the site of the former Upper Mill and the smoking chimney shaft is at the Lower Mill. At that time the main road from Chilworth to Albury followed the dam of the pond past the mill. The present road, which cuts across the pond, was opened in 1876.[13]

During the 1850s the business affairs of the Magnays ran into difficulties and in 1851 only four of the seven beating engines were working. The mills were leased to J Green but after a few months a George Cowthorpe Green, formerly of Postford Mills, was bankrupt and in a Surrey prison. He was followed by Alfred Spence in 1854 but he too was bankrupt a year later. The mills then seem to have been unoccupied. Meanwhile Sir William Magnay lived at Postford House until 1858 when he became insolvent. He then moved to Postford Cottage where he stayed until 1864. In 1865 the mills were auctioned under an order from the Sheriff of Surrey. The advertisements describe Postford Mill as having two 10 horse power high-pressure vertical steam engines, six rag engines, a 60-inch paper-making machine with three stuff chests and a cutting machine, a

52-inch paper-making machine with one stuff chest and a cutting machine, a complete set of triple-throw brass pumps, two waterwheels with wood rings, iron buckets, arms and shafts, 12 feet in diameter and 11 feet 6 inches wide, and 45 feet 6 inches of round shafting. There was also a waterwheel 17 feet in diameter and 6 feet wide driving two washing engines at the 'Upper Mill' which has been identified as the one at Postford House. Postford Mill was not included in the *Paper Mills Directory* from its first issue in 1860 up to 1871, although B Lambert was there in 1863–4 and George Adams in 1870.[14]

Pavy Pretto's Patent Felted Fabric

In 1872 Postford Mill appears in the *Paper Mills Directory* as mill 128 occupied by Pavy Pretto & Co, who were making a patent felted furniture fabric on a paper-making machine.[15] In 1871 Eugene Pavy, a Frenchman, and his partner Mr Pretto refitted the unoccupied mill and started making the new material which they called *tissus feutre japonais*. It was soon being used as curtains to decorate several archways, corridors and recesses in an exhibition at South Kensington and was reported in the journal *Engineering* as follows:

> To the casual observer these curtains appear to be very elegant Cretonnes from Mulhouse or chintzes from Manchester, but a closer examination shows them to be composed of a very different material. To the eye they are cotton goods, to the touch paper, whilst in reality they are neither but a combination of both. The fabric is firm and tough, whilst at the same time it is pliable, and is capable of being applied to many of the decorative and industrial purposes, for which paper and cotton goods, and even leather, are at present used.

The material was made from a variety of animal and vegetable fibres which were macerated in rag and beating engines, washed in alkaline and antiseptic baths, bleached, pulped and passed through vats to a papermaking machine 64 inches (163cm) wide. Powdered minerals or metals were added to the pulp to produce a sparkling effect and the fabric was finally stamped, embossed and printed. The mill had three waterwheels and together these provided 70 horse power. There were also steam engines rated at 120 horse power, steam being taken from three Cornish boilers. There were steam elevators linking the floors of the mill and a suspended overhead railway system at each level. This had points and turntables and enabled a ton or more of material to be transported easily by boys. It was said to be similar to the system in the meat-packing houses of Chicago.

The finished fabrics were sent to Messrs Pavy & Pretto's warehouse in Hamsell Street, Falcon Square, London, where they were made into curtains and other hangings. As the greatest attention was paid to economising on the materials, the manufactured articles could be sold at a low price. However it seems that they were not popular, perhaps because, as the *Journal of the Society of Arts* commented, their designs were poor. By 1876 the firm was in liquidation and other industries took over the mill.

Chilworth Paper Mills

The two mills at Chilworth appear to have stopped working for a time after Hugh Rowland, father and son, left in the early 1830s. The Little Paper Mill, excise number 388, probably did not work again. Its number was used again in 1842 but it was said to be 'left off' and the mill is not shown on the 1846 tithe map. The Great Paper Mill was discontinued as number 487 but reappeared as number 125. This was opened by Edward White in 1836 when it was described as a new mill, which suggests that it had been converted for the manufacture of machine-made paper.[16] In June 1837 James Simmons, papermaker and diarist of Haslemere, went to a sale of old equipment there, presumably from the old hand-made paper mill. The new mill itself closed by 1838 and in June 1841 James Simmons recorded that all the plant and machinery there were to be pulled down and sold.[17]

In 1846 the mill was leased to Henry Sanford for 40 years. There are contradictory reports in 1851: that three of the four beating engines were working and that number 125 had again 'left off'. It may have been occupied at about this time by a member of the well-known Spicer family of papermakers and stationers. The only evidence for this is that in 1852 a petition for bankruptcy was filed against John Edward Spicer, paper manufacturer of Chilworth and Alton.[18] The Spicers made only hand-made paper at their mill at Alton in Hampshire. They were evidently interested in working a machine mill, for Spicer Brothers displayed a roll of paper 27 inches (83 cm) wide and 2560 yards long at the Great Exhibition in 1851.[19] It is not known however where, or by whom, this was made.

The first detailed description of Chilworth paper mill as a machine mill comes from a notice in the *London Gazette* in 1855, when it was offered for sale. The tenant then was Henry Allnutt junior, who belonged to an important family of paper makers with mills in Kent and Buckinghamshire and had been at Woking mill in 1840.[20]

The 1855 sale notice describes the mill as follows:

A valuable leasehold estate producing a rental of £370 per annum, and known as the Chilworth Paper Mill, situate on the Albury stream, in the Vale of Saint Martha, near Guildford, Surrey. The buildings were erected a few years since and fitted with suitable machinery.

The mill is a substantial brick building with slated roof strongly timbered, and contains on the first floor, — an engine house, fitted with eight iron washing and beating engines, two eight-inch brass barrel pumps; large iron tank, five lead cisterns lead and copper pipes &c.; on the ground floor is the gearing to work the engines, driven by two iron water-wheels, 17 ft diameter; adjoining the engine-house is a salle and finishing rooms, fitted with two powerful hydraulic presses, with nine-inch rams and pumps; a light and lofty machine house, fitted with a highly finished paper machine, patent knotting machine, drying cylinders, set of glazing rolls, cutting machine, set of copper air-pumps &c.; a drying loft with ventilating sides, counting house, store room, foreman's dwelling, rag house, rag dusting room, and boiling house, a smith's shop, with forge and tools, a boiler house, fitted with a high pressure steam-boiler, and Jucke's patent consuming apparatus with flue communicating to a lofty brick chimney shaft; a principal's residence overlooking the premises; a detached range of buildings used as a rag store, stabling, cart-shed, and yard, enclosed by a brick wall, with a gateway entrance, gardens, orchard and paddocks; the whole standing on an area of about four acres.

The mill is supplied with pure spring water, which rises from adjoining land and flows into the premises without the aid of pumps, and the stream has a fall of 14 feet for driving the water-wheel. The premises, including the use of the machinery, are let on a lease to Mr. Henry Allnutt the Younger, at rents of £410. 10s. per annum, and are held on a lease for a term of 40 years from 25 March, 1846, at a rent of £40 per annum, and a payment of 10s. per annum for use of the spring water. The whole of the machinery, except the water-wheels subject to Mr. Allnutt's tenancy, will be included in the purchase.

A print by Henry Prosser, showing Chilworth mill as a machine mill, is reproduced in figure 42. It is undated but the fact that St Martha's church is shown in good repair suggests that it was drawn after 1850, although most of Prosser's work is earlier. The print shows shuttered drying lofts on the right, which probably survived

Figure 42 'Chilworth Paper Mills & St Martha's Surrey', by Henry Prosser, *c.*1850. The view is from the south-west. Note the drying loft on the right, the compass-armed waterwheel, the long machine room and the church on top of the hill. Courtesy of Surrey Archaeological Society.

from the earlier hand-made paper mill, the new long low building which must have housed a paper-making machine, the tall chimney indicating that steam was being used for boiling and perhaps for power, and a compass-armed waterwheel between the buildings.

The *Paper Mills Directory*, which was first published in 1860, recorded that Henry Allnutt was making tinted and coloured papers at Chilworth Mill, number 125. The 1871 edition added that he was using one machine 54 inches wide but the following year the mill appeared under the heading 'Gone out of trade in the past year'. In reality this had happened in 1870 when it was offered for sale with vacant possession. The advertisements[21] were similar to those of 1855 except that a paper-making machine 60 inches wide, driven by a 10 horse power horizontal steam engine, two bleach houses, and rag lattices and boxes are mentioned. The mills were bought not by a papermaker but by Unwin Brothers, who needed a country branch for their London-based printing firm.[22] A contemporary photograph

Figure 43 Unwin's printing works before the fire of 1895. The view is from the north-west and shows the mill house on the left, the long machine room of the former paper mill on the right and, in the distance a chimney shaft of the gunpowder works. Courtesy of Richard Unwin.

*   *   *

of the printing works is shown in figure 43. Henry Allnutt died at Alton in 1879.[23]

*   *   *

The end of papermaking at both Postford and Chilworth in 1870 was part of a trend away from small country paper mills as the scale of production increased to meet the growing demand for paper. Excise duty on paper had been abolished in 1860 and new raw materials had been found to take the place of the rags which were in short supply. The first of these, dating from about 1860, was esparto grass from Spain and North Africa. It made excellent paper. The second was timber which can either be ground to make mechanical pulp for cheap newsprint or treated chemically to produce fibrous pulp for better quality paper. These new materials were imported so mill sites nearer the ports were favoured.

Today almost all paper is made from wood pulp on large modern machines based on the early Fourdrinier models. Hand-made paper was made for the art market at Hayle Mill near Maidstone in Kent until about 1990. As an alternative, special 'mould-made' papers were introduced at the end of the nineteenth century. These simulate the quality and properties of hand-made paper but are produced on a 'cylinder mould machine' in which a cylindrical mould dips into a vat of stuff as it rotates. The paper is formed on the surface of the mould and is separated into sheets by waterproof bands on which the stuff does not settle. The sheets are then transferred to an endless felt, dried and pressed between rollers, and removed individually.[24] Paper is still made by hand by designer-craftsmen and as a museum demonstration at Wookey Hole Mill in Somerset.

Notes

1. Hills, R L, *Papermaking in Britain 1499–1988* (Athlone Press, 1988).
2. Bailey, M R, 'Robert Stephenson & Co and the Paper Drying Machine in the 1820s', *IPH Information*, vol. 23, 1989, 6–12, 51–66.
3. Coleman, D C, *The British Paper Industry, 1495–1860* (Oxford, Clarendon Press, 1958), 242.
4. Simmons Collection.
5. Minet Library 3057: Lease of Postford Mills, 28 Sept. 1832.
6. James Magnay appears in the Albury churchwarden's accounts 1827–54 (SHC: PSH/ALB/6/1); land tax records (SHC: QS6/7 Albury); Albury Parish baptism registers (SHC: PSH/ALB/3/1–2); Pigot's *Directory*, 1839.
7. *Penny Magazine Monthly Supplement*, 96 (28 Sept. 1833), 377–84.
8. *The Times*, 20 Dec. 1842, 7e.
9. Coleman, see note 3.
10. Coleman; Brayley, E W, *Topographical History of Surrey*, 1850, vol.5, App.1, 33–4.
11. Simmons Collection; SHC, Albury Parish Churchwarden's Accounts, Church Rates (PSH/ALB/6/1).
12. Weare, J, 'Postford Mills near Guildford', Guildford Museum, G 4258.
13. SHC Quarter Sessions: QS, 29 June 1875, serial no. 381; 4 April 1876, serial no. 387.
14. Simmons Collection; Greater Manchester Museum of Science and Industry: List of Paper Makers 1852; *Sussex Advertiser*, 12 Feb. 1870, 1f; *Surrey Directory*, 1855.
15. Patent no 2117, 2 July 1868: Improvements in treating and preparing certain vegetable and animal fibres; *Engineering*, 13 (31 May 1872), 373–4; *Paper Mills Directory*, 1860–84; *J Society of Arts*, Sept. 27, 1872.
16. Simmons Collection.
17. Crocker, A & Kane, M, *The Diaries of James Simmons, Paper Maker of Haslemere, 1831–1868* (Oxshott, Tabard Press, 1990), 40, 76.
18. Simmons Collection.
19. *Official Catalogue of the Great Exhibition of 1851*, vol.2, 540.
20. Simmons Collection.
21. *Sussex Advertiser*, 12 Feb. 1870, 1f.
22. Andrews, *Guildford Directory*, 1854–95; *Surrey Advertiser*, 30 Nov. 1895, 2f–h; Unwin, P, *The Printing Unwins* (George Allen & Unwin, 1976).
23. *The Times*, 2 July 1879, 1a.
24. Hills (see note 1), 110–18.

12

Chilworth Gunpowder: the Sharp Family and Marcus Westfield, 1819–1885

John Sharp, who took a lease of the powder mills from William Tinkler in 1819, was joined in partnership by his brother Thomas and then by his own son Samuel, and the firm of J T & S Sharp continued until 1881. Their London office was at 59 King William Street in the City. The business was then purchased by Charles Marcus Westfield, who had been with Messrs Hall, a long-established Kent firm which made gunpowder at Faversham and also had an engineering works at Dartford. Marcus Westfield sold his interest in the mills in 1885 when they were taken over by the new Chilworth Gunpowder Company, of which he became a director.[1] Samuel Sharp held shares in the new company.

Meanwhile the Chilworth estate had become the property of the Duke of Northumberland. William Tinkler the elder had died in 1831 aged 81[2] and his son had sold the estate in 1845 to Henry Drummond of Albury. It formed part of the marriage settlement of Drummond's daughter Louisa and Lord Lovaine, afterwards the 6th Duke, who appears as the owner on the 1847 tithe map. It remained part of the Northumberland estates until 1922, after the powder works had closed down.[3]

Records of the Wey Navigation show the quantities of gunpowder sent to London from 1827 onwards, and so cover most of the period of the Sharps' and Marcus Westfield's tenure of the works. The amount for each year is shown in figure 44. Except for the period from 1829 to 1845, when C & R Russell and then Hugh Russell ran the powder barges, cargoes were carried by the Sharps' own vessel the *Hope*, which was joined briefly by the *Faith* in 1856. On average, voyages were made once a month during the 1830s and

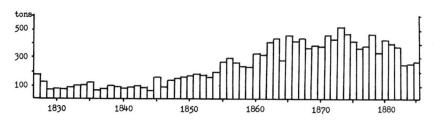

Figure 44   Tonnage of gunpowder carried on the Wey Navigation, 1827–85.

early 1840s and from then on approximately fortnightly. Saltpetre and coal, and occasionally brimstone, were carried on the return journeys.[4]

E W Brayley, writing in the 1840s, stated that the powder mills were currently out of employment,[5] but no significant gap in powder shipments during this period has been found. The increase in the 1850s coincides with the Crimean War (1853–6). That in the early 1860s may be related to modernisation of the works.

Steam-powered incorporating mills were working by 1865[6] and by 1879 there was a water turbine powering a hydraulic press. The press, by J & E Hall of Dartford, had replaced one destroyed in an explosion in 1864 and the turbine, by the German firm of Schiele, may have been installed at the same time. In 1881, when an inventory was taken,[7] the steam engine house had a 16 hp compound condensing beam engine.

Most of the process units were powered by water. In 1881 there were three incorporating mills with waterwheels, as well as a dust house, composition (mixing) house, corning house and three glazing houses. Five of the waterheels were overshot, with the water entering at the top, and were 9ft 6in (2.9m) in diameter. Those at the incorporating mills and one of the glazing houses were 24ft in diameter and were low breast-shot wheels in which the water entered just below the level of the axle.

The saltpetre refining house had 180 yards of 2in cast-iron pipes bringing water across the meadows, and various troughs, pumps, copper boilers and pans let into the floor. The brimstone refinery had a 24-inch (60 cm) diameter cast iron melting pot with furnace bars and a cast iron covering plate.

Some of the ruined structures which can be seen at Chilworth today date from this period. Several derelict waterwheel pits are crossed by the main footpath through the site and there are numer-

Figure 45   Remains of 1860s steam-powered incorporating mills. Pieces of a broken bedstone lie in the foreground. The complete bedstone behind it has space beneath to accommodate gearing. Photo by N Chitticks, 1988.

ous stone edge runners. A few remain where they stood but many have been collected together and set up as a feature alongside the path. Behind this row of stones are the remains of a steam-powered mill of the 1860s, shown in figure 45, comprising an engine bed, an intact bedstone and the remains of another bedstone broken into fragments.[8]

Explosions

Explosions at the works were not uncommon, but most were not serious. The accident of 1864 was a major one in which 30cwt of powder exploded in the press house, killing two men named Farn-field and Mansell. Afterwards work was held up for nearly three months while repairs and replacements were carried out. A local newspaper reported a visit to Filmer & Mason's iron foundry in Guildford where a new machine, to replace one destroyed in the explosion, was being made under the supervision of Mr Abraham Armitage, the foreman of the works.[9] This was a breaking-down machine, which was used to crush the mill cake before it went into the press by passing it between pairs of zinc rollers.[10] There were two further fatalities in 1864 when a powder barge blew up on the Godalming Navigation between Stonebridge and Guildford. In 1862

there had been a narrow escape at Guildford when a building caught
fire not far from a powder barge which was illegally moored in the
town.[11] In 1874 two men named Smith and Goodchild were killed
and in 1879 Goodchild's brother George and a man named Alfred
Baker were killed in another major explosion.[12]

By this time an important advance had been made in safety legislation by the Explosives Act of 1875. Many sound practices had
already evolved over the years but were not always observed for, as
counsel expressed it in the 1817 case against William Tinkler, 'the
sensations of men may be altered by custom, so that danger may
lose its terror, by becoming familiar to them'. It was recorded that
between May 1858 and June 1870 there were 29 great explosions
in powder mills, of which 9 originated in press houses, causing 44
deaths, and 11 in corning houses, also causing 44 deaths. The 1875
Act started a licensing system for factories based on the submission
of detailed plans and inspection. Chilworth was duly authorised by
Continuing Certificate No. 11 on 20 March 1876. Under the new
legislation all accidents had to be notified and were investigated by
the explosives inspectorate, whose official reports are a source of
detailed information about individual gunpowder mills and working
practices.

The report on the explosion on 18 February 1879 is such an
example. The accident was in the press house, which contained both
a hydraulic press and a breaking-down machine. Both machines
were powered by the water turbine. About 1800lbs of gunpowder
exploded, half of which was in the press.

Goodchild and Baker came to work at 7am, processed one lot of
mill cake and signalled for a second by lowering the red flag on the
building. This also signalled that the machinery had been stopped.
The mill cake was brought by boat on the millstream and the boat-
man Peter Bish took away the press cake of the previous batch. The
red flag was raised when he was 30 yards away from the building
and the machinery was set going again. As he reached the store
about 200 yards away, at 9.30am, the building blew up with a very
loud, single report. The men inside were killed instantly and their
bodies were thrown nearly 130 yards into a field to the south-west.
Parts of the machinery were hurled in all directions and debris
strewn up to 200 yards.

Mounds, screens, and the dense growth of large trees gave good
protection to other buildings on the site and there was little damage

except to windows and the light structures of the incorporating mills, which were designed to collapse easily. The incorporating mills were provided with drenching pans which overturned and emptied water over the mill bed when their balance was disturbed. Except in the more distant steam mills all of them acted. Windows were also damaged in a row of cottages 270 yards to the south and at Chilworth Manor, which was on the hill exposed to the blast, there was damage to windows and ceilings.

The inspector found that the press had been set up, with the mill cake packed in layers between the copper plates, but the pressure was not fully on and he concluded that the explosion had originated in the breaking-down machine. This was the machine that had been made by Filmer & Mason of Guildford in 1864. It was an improved design in which the zinc rollers would automatically move apart over any obstruction and spring back into place. It was a well-tried machine, as was the 1864 press by Messrs Hall of Dartford. The workmen were reliable and experienced, and reported by Peter Bish to have been sober and proceeding in the normal way.

The inspector found that working practice was generally good. There were a few weak points but he could not say that any of these was the cause of the accident. He suggested a few improvements — a fence around the works for security, regular inspections of men and clothing, regular overhauling of machinery, better precautions against foreign substances getting into the process, and stricter rules about taking food and drink into danger buildings. The verdict of the jury at the inquest was that the deceased met their deaths by an explosion of gunpowder in a press house but that the cause of the accident had not been proved.[13]

There was a less serious explosion on 15 November 1883 which injured a millman named David Smithers. The official report describes the incorporating mills at this time as having two powerful edge rollers or runners revolving slowly round a central axis in a large basin or mill pan. The runners were made of stone with thick iron tyres. The mill bed and the curb — the side of the mill pan — were also made of iron. The central hub through which the runners were connected also supported two wooden ploughs which travelled around in front of each runner, turning the charge into its path, one inwards and one outwards since the runners were arranged asymmetrically. The mill was powered by steam and driven by gearing from below.

The whole apparatus tended to become clogged with incrusted powder which had to be removed daily. Smithers was 'paddling off' this material with a long-handled copper 'spud' when it ignited and set off 50lb of unworked powder — the 'green charge' — which was lying in small heaps on the bed, ready to be spread out when the cleaning was finished. It was found that the incrusted powder had not been moistened sufficiently and that not enough care had been taken with the copper implement. The inspector pointed out that there was a common but erroneous impression, even among experienced powder hands, that copper and brass tools were safe. However, many accidents had occurred with them, and even with wooden tools, because not only sparks but percussion could generate enough heat to cause gunpowder to explode. Smithers had suffered burns to his face and hands but had been spared worse injuries by the protective clothing with ear-flaps with which mill hands were provided. The mill building, a wooden structure 15 feet square, had all its boards stripped and blown in all directions up to about 27 yards, but the trees around it had stopped some of the fragments. The principle structure of the building had remained intact but an iron tyre and a plough were damaged. Another mill nearby was also ignited, probably by burning debris rather than by the explosion itself, as there was an interval of a few seconds which allowed the man inside it to escape.[14]

The Old Manor House

Chilworth Manor, the historic mansion house of the estate, is on the south-facing slopes below St Martha's church. The large house at the south end of Blacksmith Lane known as the Old Manor House was called Powder Mill House on the 1846 tithe map.

The house presents a puzzle. A datestone of 1609 over the north doorway seems at odds with both the history of the estate and the style of the building. Thomas Steere, the would-be wire manufacturer, had been made to close his works three years before this and the East India Company was yet to arrive. It might be expected that a substantial house would be built during their tenure or when Charles I financed the expansion of the mills in 1636. As shown in figure 46, the oldest part of the house has brick-built gables typical of the Dutch style of architecture which became fashionable in England in the 1630s. The earliest example in England is at Kew Palace, known also as the Dutch House, built by a London merchant Samuel

Figure 46   The Old Manor House, formerly Powder Mill House to which was attached the dwelling house of the Little Paper Mill. The view is from the north-east, showing the original building, with Dutch gables, at the right, and later extensions at the left. Photo by Glenys Crocker.

Fortrey in 1631. The style is also represented in Surrey by 1630s work at West Horsley Place and Slyfield Manor near Stoke D'Abernon.[15] It would be remarkable indeed if it reached Chilworth so much earlier.

In 1728 the dwelling house of the Little Paper Mill, which was then let to Mr Gay and Mr Wadking, was part of the Powder Mill House. The building was still in two parts when the estate was sold in 1813 but by then the papermakers' portion was described as 'an old dwelling house adjoining to the Powder Mill House, brick and timber, and tiled, now let in three tenements'. This matches the plan of Powder Mill House on the 1846 tithe map, which has three small divisions along the south side.[16]

A Sharp family photograph, thought to date from the 1860s,[17] shows the same north-east facing aspect of the house as figure 46. The major extensions in the photograph had not yet been built and on the 1871 Ordnance Survey map the ground plan is still like that of 1846. The 1896 edition shows a large extension on the east side. Local directories record the Sharp family at the powder mills until 1881, the year in which they sold the gunpowder business to Marcus Westfield. They appear in 1881 at the private address of 'Tanglemere' or Tangley Mere and by 1887 Powder Mill House has become the Old Manor House and is occupied by people associated

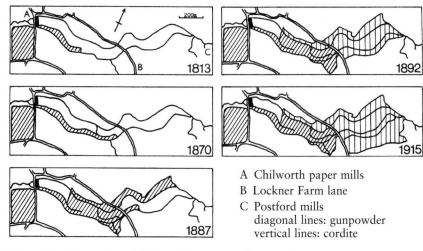

Figure 47   Expansion of Chilworth powder mills, 1813–1915.

with the new Chilworth Gunpowder Company.[18] It seems likely that the house was extended by Westfield or his successors and was dignified with old architectural details and a new name at the same time.

*   *   *

The expansion of the gunpowder works after 1813 is shown in the sequence of sketch maps in figure 47. The steam-powered mills, still making traditional black gunpowder, began the expansion eastwards in the 1860s and between 1885 and the First World War the works again spread up the valley to Postford.

Notes

1. SHC, Royal Naval Exhibition 1891, Chilworth Gunpowder Company (G132/5/2).
2. St Martha's Parish Registers, burials 7 Dec 1831.
3. Albury Estate Office. Outlying portions of the Albury Estate, Surrey, for auction July 20 and 21, 1922.
4. SHC, Wharfinger's diary, 1848–57 (G142/2/2); Wey Navigation diaries, Thames Lock down traffic 1827–1940 (G129/2/11–16); Wood, D, 'Hope from above Guildford', Topsail, vol.17 (Spring 1978), 34–7.
5. Brayley, E W & Britton, J, *Topographical history of Surrey*, vol.5 [c.1848], 131.
6. Murray's *Handbook for Surrey* (1865), 56.
7. Schedule prepared for Duke of Northumberland, 1881.
8. Crocker, G, *A Guide to the Chilworth Gunpowder Mills* (3rd edn, 1999).
9. The Times, 6 August 1864; *The Local Journal*, 25 October 1864. The names of the victims are in *Surrey Advertiser*, 10 Feb 1901.

10. *Parliamentary Papers*, 1878/9, xvi, 377.

11. Vine, P, *London's Lost Route to the Sea* (David & Charles, 1965), 152–3.

12. *Godalming Almanack and Directory* (Chennel, 1875), 1; *Surrey Advertiser*, 10 Feb 1901.

13. *Parliamentary Papers*, 1878/9, xvi, 377.

14. *Parliamentary Papers*, 1884, xvii, 675.

15. Nairn, I & Pevsner, N, *Surrey* (Penguin, Buildings of England, 1962), 278, 388–9, 430; Summerson, J, *Architecture in Britain, 1530–1830* (Penguin, 1953), 53, 92, pl.56b.

16. SHC, Chilworth estate sale particulars 1813 (G85/2/1(2) no.4); Tithe map, 1846.

17. Information from John and Christine Baden.

18. Ordnance Survey 25 inch (1:2500) map, Surrey sheet 32.5, 1871 and 1896; *Andrews' Guildford Directory*.

13

Brown Powder and Cordite

As larger guns were introduced in the 19th century, new propellants were needed. At first, development work concentrated on black powder, by varying its composition to suit different classes of fire-arms. Also, to control the rate of burning, it was made up into blocks such as hexagonal prisms with holes down the middle and in that form was known as 'prismatic powder'. Another important invention was that of brown or 'cocoa' powder. This was made in the traditional way but the charcoal was made from straw and gave off less smoke than black powder. It had great success but only for a short time, as it was soon overtaken by developments in high explosives.

The Chilworth Gunpowder Company and Cocoa Powder

The invention of brown prismatic powder was claimed by J N Heidemann and Max von Duttenhofer in Germany, though they were not alone in the field, and their product was made by Vereinigte Rheinisch-Westphälische Pulverfabriken. In 1883 the invention was taken up by the British authorities and arrangements were made for the superintendent of the Royal Gunpowder Factory at Waltham Abbey to be instructed in its manufacture. To make the product, the Chilworth Gunpowder Company was formed in March 1885 as a subsidiary of the German company. It acquired Marcus Westfield's interest in the works for £20,476 9s 3d and took a lease of the site for 21 years. The new company was under German control but with Lord Sudeley as Chairman. Heidemann and Duttenhofer were on the board of directors and Westfield became joint managing director together with Edward Kraftmeier, the London agent of Vereinigte Rheinisch-Westphälische Pulverfabriken. Duttenhofer and Heide-

Figure 48 Chilworth powder mills: the view south from St Martha's Hill, from *Wyman's Commercial Encyclopaedia*, 1888. The chimney stack on the left is at the 1885 brown powder incorporating mills, the central one is at the 1860s steam-powered incorporating mills (see figure 45), and the one at the right is in the raw-materials processing area west of Blacksmith Lane. The internal tramway system is shown and the railway line, with a terrace of cottages (which survives) and a steam locomotive, can be seen in the middle distance.

mann each held 1990 shares, Sudeley 10 and Westfield, Kraftmeier and Sharp, who had sold the business to Westfield in 1881, held 150 each.[1]

Major work on new buildings was started in June 1885 and by 1887 Westfield was seeking permission to build new magazines on land to the east, to store the increased quantities of brown powder which were being made.[2] In December 1888 an agreement was made with the South Eastern Railway Company to build a tramway link to a siding at Chilworth and Albury station. No records survive of goods transported by rail but the Navigation records show a dramatic increase in the amount of gunpowder sent by barge in the years when brown powder was being produced. The tonnage increased from an average of 230 tons each year in 1883–5 to 400 in 1886, 780 in 1887 and an average of 1400 tons each year in 1888–90.[3] It therefore appears that gunpowder was still sent by the Navigation and the railway was used for bringing in coal, principally for the steam engines.

A contemporary view of the works as seen from a point near St Martha's church is reproduced in figure 48. This comes from an article in *Wyman's Commercial Encyclopaedia* for 1888, which describes the contemporary business scene by taking an example of each industry featured. Wymans had no difficulty in selecting Chilworth for their article on gunpowder. The drawing shows three chimney shafts, each nearly 150ft high, which were linked to boilers working twelve steam engines, several of up to 100hp. There were also waterwheels and water turbines. The picture also shows tramways which, together with the mill stream along the southern edge of the site, provided transport between the various buildings. The extension of the tramway to the station had not yet been built. The buildings were widely spaced and surrounded by trees to minimise the damage from any explosion.

Between 300 and 400 workers were employed, many of them army reserve men and old soldiers recruited from the National Association for the Employment of Reserve Soldiers. The Company had opened a second factory at Fernilee near Buxton in Derbyshire and it had magazines on the Thames, at Liverpool and in many other places. Work went on night and day.[4]

The Company took part in the Royal Naval Exhibition at the Camperdown Gallery in 1891 and its brochure[5] included an extract from the Wyman's article illustrated by the view of the works. The exhibits included a full assortment of sporting and blasting powders and the chief varieties of military powder. The chief products were various kinds of prismatic powder — black, 'cocoa' or brown and 'what is specially known as 'prismatic E.X.E.' Dummy cartridges were shown of the exact sizes for 110 ton, 80 ton, 12 ton and 6-inch guns, and samples of cases and cylinders for storing and transporting powder on land and at sea. The exhibit of greatest interest however was a new product known as smokeless powder, which was to bring about the next stage of expansion of the works.

The area of the site developed in the late 1880s is shown in the sketch map in figure 47. The manufacturing area now extended up the valley east of the Lockner Farm lane, mainly along the north bank of the Tillingbourne. There are many ruined features of this period, some of them badly decayed and hidden in undergrowth. The two most substantial features are the 1885 incorporating mills and the tramway swing bridge.

The row of six steam-powered incorporating mills erected in 1885 (fig 49) was conserved by Guildford Borough Council in the 1990s. Each of the six compartments contained an iron incorporating mill as shown in figure 50. These were of German manufacture, as were

Figure 49 Ruins of part of the 1885 brown powder incorporating mills. There were six chambers with a light-weight roof and front wall. Battens for matchboarding can be seen on the walls and the device at roof level is part of a system of levers and rods for operating a safety drenching mechanism in each chamber. The entrance is to a tunnel from which the equipment on either side was controlled. Photo by Gareth Crocker, 1983.

the girders, which bear the maker's mark 'Burbach 1884'. There are remnants of the matchboarding which covered the walls, to ensure that no particles which could cause friction fell into the machinery, and traces of the lightweight roofing material designed to give way in any explosion. The front walls were also of light construction, to direct any blast forward, away from the boiler and engine house at the rear of the building and to minimise damage to the main structure and the machinery inside. The levers at roof level, connected by rods, were for operating a drenching mechanism. An explosion in one mill caused a tank of water to tip over and triggered the mechanism in the other compartments so that all the mills were drenched. The steam engine at the rear operated a line-shaft along the back of the building which probably drove the mills from below by belts. The mills were controlled from the ends of the building and from tunnels between pairs of compartments.[6]

The swing bridge (figure 51) was built to carry the 1888 tramway link to the station across the 1652–4 New Cut millstream. It can be seen alongside the modern footbridge where Vera's Path enters the

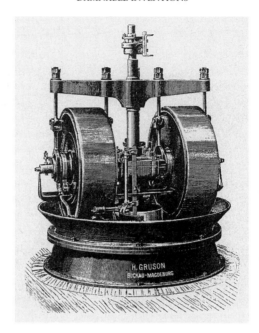

Figure 50 Iron incorporating mill by Gruson of Magdeburg, Germany. One of these was installed in each of the six chambers of the 1885 brown powder mill building shown in figure 49.

Figure 51 The swing bridge which carried a branch of the works' tramway to Chilworth and Albury station. The timber portion in the foreground is fixed but the iron portion opened to allow punts to pass through. Photograph by Glenys Crocker during a guided tour of the site in the 1980s.

Figure 52   Punts on the mill stream, 1913. The barrels of powder in the punt on the left are covered with leather. Photo courtesy of A Hammond.

site from a point near the school on the Dorking road. It has a fixed timber half and an iron portion which pivoted, to allow punts to pass through. The footpaths through the site follow the line of the tramways and a few timber sleepers can still be seen underfoot. Although horses were used in many gunpowder works the trams at Chilworth were pushed by men. The tramway had a continental gauge of 800mm (2ft 7½in). It can be seen in the foreground of the group photograph of workmen on the front cover of this book.[7] The only other surviving photograph of men at work is reproduced in figure 52 and shows two men transporting barrels of powder in a punt. Both these photographs date from about 1913. By then the factory had greatly expanded to manufacture new products, and further expansion was to come in the First World War.

High Explosives and 'Smokeless Powder'
The smokeless powder shown at the Royal Naval exhibition in 1891 was the product of new technology. Unlike gunpowder — both traditional black powder and the new brown powder of the 1880s — which was incorporated mechanically, the new high explosives, and the propellants based on them, were made by chemical means. There

had been two parallel developments, based on the nitration of cellu-
lose and of glycerine, both of which were first carried out in 1846.
The development of nitrocellulose or guncotton suffered an early
set-back because of several disastrous explosions in 1847. The problem was tackled by von Lenk in Austria and by Abel in Britain but
it was not until 1872 that guncotton was approved by the British
government and went into production at Waltham Abbey. Meanwhile, Nobel took up the problem of the detonation of nitroglycerine
and produced dynamite in 1864 and blasting gelatine in 1875.

In the 1880s success was achieved in controlling the force of the
new explosives for ballistic use. The new propellants were known as
'smokeless powders'. The first of these was a nitrocellulose propellant called '*Poudre B*' which was invented in France by Vieille in
1886. In the following year Nobel patented ballistite, a nitroglycer-
ine-nitrocellulose mixture. The British Government set up an Explosives Committee in 1888 and in 1889 two of its members, Abel and
Dewar, patented cordite, a mixture of nitrocellulose and nitroglycerine extruded in the form of strings or cords, hence its name. Chemically cordite was closely related to ballistite and Nobel brought an
unsuccessful legal action against its manufacturers for infringing his
patent. Other synthetic explosives were developed from dyestuff
intermediates, including lyddite (picric acid or trinitrophenol) and
TNT (trinitrotoluene).[8]

With the invention of smokeless powders the explosives and propellants industries, which had been developing separately, became
technologically linked. The dynamite manufacturers and the powder
makers therefore began to combine. Chilworth, as a subsidiary of
the German company, came within the scope of a General Pooling
Agreement made in 1889 between four German companies known
as the 'powder group' and a dynamite group consisting of the
London-based Nobel Dynamite Trust and its subsidiaries in Germany, Britain and South America.

In 1901, Vickers acquired a 40 per cent interest in Chilworth as
part of a trading agreement. In 1905 the Company was involved in
setting up the Japanese Explosives Co Ltd of which it owned 20 per
cent. Chilworth became wholly British during the First World War,
in 1915, when the Nobel Dynamite Trust was split up and liquid-
ated.[9]

Some non-technical details of the Chilworth products are provided
by the 1891 exhibition brochure. The range of smokeless powders

shown, as dummy replicas, alongside the established products varied from fine sporting powder to cubes of three quarters of an inch surface and were recommended for magazine rifles and all guns up to the 9.2-inch breech-loader. Although these products had been developed, the new Smokeless Powder factory for their manufacture at Chilworth was not built until 1892.

The Company's entry in *The Rise and Progress of the British Explosives Industry* published in 1909 states that it was at Chilworth that cordite was first manufactured by a private company, clients having been supplied with cordite before the Government adopted it. The Government approved cordite in 1893 and the first contracts with private companies were awarded in 1894. Chilworth was allocated 2 per cent of the contracts in 1899–1900 and about 10 per cent in the years leading up to the war in 1914. The description of Chilworth in 1909 states that explosives were manufactured for home and foreign consumption. There were magazines and agents in all the principal colonies and agents in all principal foreign countries. The mills were producing 'all classes of propellent smokeless powders for military and sporting purposes, and gunpowder ordinarily so-called'. The entry states that there were factories at Chilworth and Fernilee and the description of the manufacturing plant and the numbers employed may refer to both combined. There were 143 buildings, steam engines totalling 1500 hp and water power of about 100 hp, about five miles of tramway and three 10-ton weighbridges. There were about 300 male and 6 female workers, one head and one assistant chemist, two chief and assistant engineers and 20 manufacturing, commercial and administrative employees.[10]

The new smokeless powder factory at Chilworth was built east of the gunpowder works, as shown in figure 47, and the two factories continued to operate side by side but separately. However a worker recalled that steam was taken from the boiler house behind the 1885 incorporating mills into the smokeless powder works. The manufacture of cordite involved kneading together the nitrocellulose and nitroglycerine with acetone as a solvent and forcing the paste through dies of the required diameter. Some of the acetone was recovered before drying was completed and finally the cordite was blended by putting together different lots.

The most striking of the process buildings which survives is the kneading and press house (figure 53), a long brick building with tall

Figure 53 The brick press house of the 1890s cordite factory from the east. The tall compartments housed accumulators for hydraulic presses. Drawing by Rowena Oliver.

compartments to house the accumulators for hydraulic presses. There are also two drying stoves, an acetone recovery stove with the words 'DRYING AND EXTRACTION OF SOLVENTS' still decipherable on its wall and a packing house. All these structures are on private land and inaccessible but the kneading and press house comes into view from the public footpath which runs from the Lockner Farm lane to Postford Pond. The Chilworth works specialised in finishing the manufacture of cordite. There was no nitration plant for producing guncotton and nitroglycerine on site as cordite paste was obtained from the Nobel Explosives Company factory at Ardeer in Ayrshire.[11] Testing of products was carried out away from the site at Pirbright, on land leased from the War Department.[12]

When cordite replaced brown powder as the most successful smokeless propellant, from about 1892 onwards, there was a drop in the amount of 'powder' carried on the Wey Navigation. The largest amount in a year was about 1500 tons in 1890 and this fell to 1000 in 1891 and 500 in 1892. The annual total then fluctuated between 200 and 500 tons per year until 1908. It therefore seems likely that the new products were transported by rail, for which there are no records, and that the black powder which was still being manufactured continued to go by barge. The tramway in the smokeless powder works crossed the lane into the black powder site and was hence linked to the station. From 1908 onwards the tonnage of 'powder' carried on the Navigation increased to a maximum of 1366 tons in 1914, when the First World War began. The figures then cease to look meaningful and no shipments were recorded from 1917 onwards, except for a small amount in 1920.[13]

The Admiralty Cordite Works

The final stage in the development of the works was the building of a second cordite factory by the Admiralty in 1915, during the First World War. It was situated south of the 1890s cordite works and south of the mill stream, in fields now crossed by a public footpath. Like the 1890s cordite factory it specialised in finishing cordite from ready-prepared cordite paste.[14] It was served by an internal tramway but this was separate from that of the earlier factory and it was recalled that the finished cordite was loaded on to carts, and later a steam lorry, at the Lockner farm lane and taken to the station by road.[15]

A plan of the Admiralty works, with a key to the various buildings, is shown in figure 54. A solvent recovery stove, divided into four bays, is the only building with walls still standing at the beginning of the twenty-first century. It had a barrel-shaped roof, as did

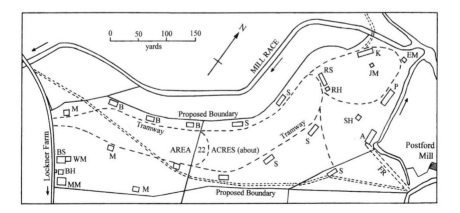

Figure 54 Plan of the proposed Admiralty cordite factory based on an original in the Northumberland archives at Alnwick. A: acetone store, B: Blending house; BH: boot house; BS: box store; EM: expense magazine; JM: jelly-melting house; K: kneading house; M: magazine; MM: men's mess room; P: press house; RH: recovery house; RS: recovery stove; S: stove; SH: still house; WM: women's mess room. Foundations of most of these buildings survive close to the sites shown.

Figure 55 Cottages converted *c.*1920 from the press house of the Admiralty cordite works (P in figure 54). The partitions and shape of the original roof are clearly visible. The cottages were demolished and replaced by Postford Mill Cottages in the 1980s. Photo by Glenys Crocker.

the cordite press house. This was converted into a terrace of five cottages, shown in figure 55, before the Duke of Northumberland sold the site in 1922. They were demolished in the 1980s and the new Postford Mill Cottages built in their place. Of the other buildings, only the foundations can still be seen.[16]

Notes

1. SHC, Chilworth Gunpowder Company, Prospectus, 1885 (G132/3).
2. Northumberland Estates Office, Alnwick, correspondence.
3. Albury Estates, sale particulars, 1922. Thanks are due to Alan Wardell for information from the Guildford 'Down' diaries in the Wey Navigation records: SHC, G129/3/14–15.
4. *Wymans Commercial Encyclopaedia for 1888*, (Wymans, London); Winfield, J, *The gunpowder mills of Fernilee* (Whaley Bridge, the author, 1996).
5. SHC, Royal Naval Exhibition

1891, The Chilworth Gunpowder Company Ltd (G132/5/2).
6. Crocker, G, *A Guide to the Chilworth Gunpowder Mills* (SIHG, 3rd edn 1999).
7. Crocker, A, 'The Tramway at the Chilworth Gunpowder Works', *SyAC*, vol.82 (1994), 181–95.
8. Simmons, W H, *A Short History of the Royal Gunpowder Factory at Waltham Abbey* (Royal Ordnance Factories, 1963); Hardie, D W F & Pratt, J D, *A History of the Modern British Chemical Industry* (1966).
9. Reader, W J, *Imperial Chemical Industries: a History. Volume 1:*

The Forerunners, 1870–1926 (Oxford, 1970).

10. *The Rise and Progress of the British Explosives Industry*, ed. E A Brayley Hodgetts (7th International Congress of Applied Chemistry, Whittaker, 1909), 344–6.

11. Cocroft, W, *Dangerous Energy* (English Heritage, 2000).

12. SHC: Pirbright Poor Rate, 1896.

Trevor Cobley is thanked for this information.

13. Information from Alan Wardell (see note 3).

14. Cocroft, see note 11.

15. Information from the late Jim Puddick; A Crocker, see note 7.

16. NEO Alnwick, plan of proposed Admiralty works; G Crocker, see note 6.

14

The Great Explosion and Other Memories

The accident at the black powder corning house on 12 February 1901, in which six men lost their lives, was the worst explosion on record at Chilworth. A memorial card for the victims is reproduced as figure 56.

There were two explosions, the first in a tram outside the corning house setting off the second in the building itself. The iron rails of the tramway stopped five yards short of the building, according to

Figure 56 Memorial card for the victims of the 1901 explosion. Courtesy of Ron Puddick.

a rule which had been badly worded and interpreted too literally. It was the intention that the track should continue with wooden rails but at Chilworth it simply stopped and the powder was carried the rest of the way. The ground was frozen and it was thought that one of the men had slipped on his hob-nailed boots, making a spark which ignited the powder in the tram. No Home Office regulation had been contravened, but the Company decided to make some changes, in particular to provide more suitable footwear in future.[1] The local press reported the accident in detail. The two men who were not killed instantly, William Sopp and George Smithers, were taken to the private hospital in the works, where they died soon afterwards, and a workshop on the site was used as a mortuary for the remains of the others. The inquest was held in the Percy Arms public house.[2]

A few years earlier, in November 1895, a major disaster had been threatened at the powder mills when the neighbouring Unwin's printing works, shown in figure 43, caught fire. The blaze, caused by sparks from the foundry chimney, started at about half-past-ten on a Saturday evening. The Gunpowder Company's fire brigade was first on the scene and set two of its engines to work on the fire while the third pumped water on to the factory magazine. This, though not full to its capacity of 60 tons, contained a large quantity of powder and was down-wind from the inferno. The Guildford fire brigade arrived at half-past-eleven and the one from Shere a quarter of an hour later. A storeroom at the powder works containing packing cases caught fire and the north-east wind blew burning paper on to the magazine. Fortunately the Albury fire brigade arrived in time to avert what would have been a massive explosion but the printing works was totally destroyed.[3] Its charred ruins are shown in figure 57.

A copy of the safety code for the smokeless powder (cordite) factory survives from 1916. Employees were searched on arrival to ensure that no matches or iron objects were brought in. They changed into specially-provided working clothes with no metal buttons, pockets or turn-ups. 'Magazine boots' were provided in danger buildings to avoid contact with grit, and all benches and floors of danger buildings were frequently swept and kept clean. Containers were always to be lifted, not dragged, to avoid friction. The quantities of explosives and ingredients which could be held in buildings were strictly limited and temperatures were carefully monitored and

Figure 57 Unwins' printing works after the fire in November 1895. The view is from the west and the ruins of the long building of figure 43 are on the left. Photograph courtesy of Richard Unwin.

controlled. Machinery was inspected daily and had to be stopped instantly when out of order.

There were further rules for persons carrying out repairs, who had to observe strict formalities. After permission had been obtained in writing, the building, machinery and ground outside had to be saturated with water and all woodwork thoroughly washed with acetone before any work began. The rule book was signed by E Kay, Managing Director, and by Major E Cooper Key, H M Chief Inspector of Explosives at the Home Office.

*   *   *

The managing director E Kay was in fact Edward Kraftmeier who, like several of the German personnel, had settled into the local community and become naturalised. The works manager, Captain Otto Bouvier, and Heinrich Wirths, one of the foremen, both appear in the photograph of the Company's cricket team reproduced in figure 58, which was taken in 1893. Otto Bouvier lived at the Old Manor House from 1887 onwards and died in 1906 at the age of 59. His grave, inside a cast-iron railing near the south-west corner of St Martha's church, also bears inscriptions to

Figure 58 The Chilworth Gunpowder Company cricket team, 1893. From left to right, back row: C Smith, A Whitbourn, R Lemon, E Hill, J Hayes, H Wirths, Capt Otto Bouvier; middle row: L Mercer, W Payne, J Cannon, E Randall; front row: E Payne, J Atfield. Photo courtesy of Blackheath Cricket Club.

his wife and two of their children who died in the 1930s. Wirths' son died in the war, serving as an air mechanic in the Royal Flying Corps, and as Henry Walter Wirth is among the names on the Chilworth war memorial.

The Company played a major role in the celebrations for Queen Victoria's Diamond Jubilee in 1897. Captain Bouvier and Mr W and Mr A Hartmann, who were major stock-holders in the Company and lived at Tangley Mere, were vice-presidents of the committee. Mr Wirths was among the stewards at the sports and dinner which were held at the Company's cricket ground. This was on the east side of Blacksmith Lane at its junction with the Dorking Road. In the evening there was a torchlight procession to St Martha's where the Chilworth party was joined by one from Albury and a bonfire was lit. The Company provided 24 magnesium lights and eighty maroons, or flash bombs, for the Royal Salute.[4]

For a short time in the 1890s, employees of the gunpowder

mills and the printing works had a social centre at the Gresham-bury Institute. This is a building of unusual and striking design by the architect W H Seth-Smith which stands on the north side of the main road of the village. It became the Anglican church of St Thomas's in 1896 and is still used regularly for worship.[5]

The workforce numbered between 300 and 400 by the end of the nineteenth century but housing was provided only for some of the more senior employees. Most of the workers walked from nearby villages — Shalford, Blackheath and Wonersh and over the Downs from Merrow. The Company built a terrace of five cottages near the 1890s smokeless powder factory which was later converted into the single residence called Longfrey. With its decorative barge-boards the present house can be seen facing south over the valley. A former worker recalled that the Wirths, who were a large family, occupied two of the Longfrey cottages. At the western end of the works, near the Old Manor House, 'Magazine Cottages' were built in the 1890s as a row of four and a row of three dwellings.

Memorabilia
A few old photographs, objects and letters have been kept by families associated with the works. Memories have been related by several local people whose fathers or grandfathers worked at the factory and by a few women who worked there in the First World War and lived into the 1980s.

Mrs Eyre, for example, identified the man beside the lamp-post on the cover photograph as her father, Charlie Brownjohn of Merrow, whom she recognised from his hand: he had lost several fingers in 1910 in a mangle in the cordite factory and afterwards worked on the punts. He was employed from 1882, when he was aged 16, until about 1920 when he earned 30 shillings per week. He worked 12-hour day or night shifts. The workers had bank holidays and there was a works outing by train to the seaside.

Some items of memorabilia are shown in figure 59. The Chilworth Gunpowder Company label is from a canister, a rare survival. Examples are known mainly in museums in Australia, where gun-powder was greatly in demand among settlers and fortune-seekers in the early days, and in a few private collections. The Cricket Club

Figure 59 Memorabilia. *Above left*: Label from a rare Chilworth gunpowder canister; note the erroneous claim that the mills were established in 1570. Photo courtesy of Jim Buchanan. *Above right*: Cricket Club fixtures card, 1912 (original coloured red). Photo courtesy of H Booth. *Below*: Presentation glass model tram (15cm long). Courtesy of Ron Puddick.

card diplays a badge derived from the Company's characteristic product, brown prismatic powder. It lists the club's fixtures which were held on Saturday afternoons and bank holidays. The glass tram was presented to Mr Edward Puddick after 25 years' service at the mills. He had started work in 1889, received a redundancy notice in 1897 when there was a lack of orders, but returned and had completed 32 years' service when the final notice of closure came in 1921. The model tram was mass-produced in pressed glass by a firm at Newcastle-upon-Tyne and represents a colliery tram, but it evidently bore an acceptable likeness to the powder-works trams at Chilworth.[6]

There was a scheme, run on a voluntary basis by one of the foremen, Mr Trice, whereby men paid into a fund to provide sick-pay. Wages were low because of the employment of many ex-soldiers, who were already in receipt of a pension, and discontentment arose in 1913 which resulted in the formation of a Workers' Union.[7]

The First World War

The factory was provided with anti-aircraft guns by early 1915[8] and St Martha's church was camouflaged with branches. During air raids the women took shelter at Postford Mill and the men went to Lockner Holt.

The worst scare was in 1915 when a Zeppelin dropped twelve bombs in the St Catherine's area of Guildford on the night of Wednesday 13 October 1915 and there was, and still is, a widespread belief that it was looking for the gunpowder works. There was damage to property but the only casualties were a swan on the river and 17 chickens. An official German message, received at Amsterdam on the following day, said of the night's raids, by five airships: 'Our naval airships, on the night of October 13, attacked London's important establishments and batteries at Ipswich. The City of London, the London Docks, the waterworks at Hampton near London, and Woolwich were lavishly bombarded.' William Oakley, author of *Guildford in the Great War*, observed that the objective of the Zeppelins was to bomb targets in London and was inclined to think that the one over Guildford had simply strayed farther west than intended and was lost.[9]

Over 600 people worked at the factory during the First World War, many walking or cycling to work from Guildford. The workforce included many women who typically had been in domestic service previously. Several formal studio photographs survive of women in their navy serge working uniforms, such as figure 60, which convey a sense of pride and status in their work. They worked both day and night shifts but few of them entered the danger buildings. Mrs Makins, whose father Dennis Parry worked at the black powder factory for 36 years, remembered carrying trays of cordite between buildings. Her pay was 4d per hour. Many at the cordite factory suffered from headaches when

Figure 60 Studio portrait of two women workers at the cordite factory in the First World War. Fanny Elizabeth Cumper (right) has been identified by her niece, Mrs Nancy Crick. Her colleague on the left is thought to be Florence Hughes. Photo courtesy of Pat Saunders.

they first began work there but most became adjusted to the conditions. There were men's and women's mess rooms where workers prepared their meals. A rare hint of the social life that must have existed is provided by the photograph of a women's football team, reproduced as figure 61.

The End
A letter dated 16 June 1920 from the managing director T G Tulloch, informed employees of the impending closure of the works. Thomas Tulloch had joined the Chilworth Gunpowder

Figure 61 Chilworth gunpowder works women's football team. Photo by Scribb entitled 'Pioneer Ladies F C, Mr Hammond's team'. Courtesy of Bill Bailey.

Company in 1904, after retiring from a successful career in the army. He was active in the development of munitions and was known especially for his promotion of TNT, which earned him the nickname 'Trinitro Tom', and of chain-track traction, or tanks.[10] His letter to the Chilworth workforce explained that there had been a fall in demand for gunpowder since the Armistice and that British companies could not compete with producers in Belgium and America.

The closure was in fact part of a rationalisation of the explosives industry by Explosives Trades Limited, into which the leading companies merged after the war. The new company became Nobel Industries Limited in 1920 and was itself to become part of Imperial Chemical Industries in 1926.[11]

The Chilworth workers received £5 for each year of their employment when the works closed. One of the employees, Mr G Trice, who had organised the scheme for sick pay, made a new career establishing a local bus service, which became the well-known Tillingbourne Bus Company.[12]

A former employee recalled that some of the equipment was sold to an Argentine manufacturer and that at least two men went to Argentina to help to set it up. There is also evidence that some of the incorporating mills went to Faversham and from there to Ardeer in Ayrshire. Nobel Industries decided to concentrate production at the Oare and Marsh Works at Faversham and in 1928 four of the eight incorporating mills at the Oare Works were known as the 'Chilworth' mills. Black gunpowder continued to be made at Faversham until the 1930s but it was then moved, for safety, to the Nobel works at Ardeer. Eight incorporating mills from Oare were sent there and, unless the Oare mills had been renewed, which is unlikely in the circumstances of the time, would have included those which had come from Chilworth.[13]

Notes

Some of the information in this chapter was provided by former workers or their descendants. A detailed account of the 1901 explosion, a substantial extract from the 1922 sale particulars, and full transcripts of the 1916 *Rules* and Tulloch's letter of 16 June 1920 are given in D W Warner's article 'The Great Explosion and the Later History of the Chilworth Gunpowder Mills' in *Surrey History*, vol.1 no.4 (1976), 131–57. Note that the map on pp.148–9 which is there dated 1922, actually pre-dates the 1888 tramway link to the station and was merely re-used for the sale.

1. *Parliamentary Papers*, 1901, ix, 815.
2. *Surrey Advertiser*, 16 February, 1901; Warner (see above).
3. *Surrey Advertiser*, 30 November, 1895.
4. *Surrey Advertiser*, August 1897.
5. Nairn, I & Pevsner, N, *Surrey* (Buildings of England, 1962), 135.
6. Crocker, A, 'The Tramway at the Chilworth Gunpowder Works', *SyAC*, vol.82 (1994), 181-95.
7. Warner (see above), 150, from information provided by a Mr Edwards.
8. Cocroft, W, *Dangerous Energy* (English Heritage, 2000).
9. Oakley, W H, *Guildford in the Great War: the Record of a Surrey Town* (Guildford, Billing & Sons Ltd, 1934), 146–162.
10. Information provided by John Glanfield.
11. Reader, W J, *Imperial Chemical Industries, a History: vol. 1 The Forerunners 1870–1926* (Oxford, 1970).
12. King, B, *Tillingbourne: 1924–1974. The Story of 50 years of Independent Bus Operation in West Surrey* (1974).
13. Patterson, E M, *Gunpowder Manufacture at Faversham: Oare and Marsh Factories* (Faversham Papers No. 42, 1995), 6.

15

Post-script

The paper mills of the Tillingbourne valley closed by about 1870 and their sites were redeveloped or became private gardens, so that no distinctive traces remain. The gunpowder works continued for fifty years longer and, because their structures were numerous and spread out along the valley, more have survived, if only in a ruined or fragmentary state.

The Paper Mills

Charles Ball's departure from Albury Park Mill in 1810 coincided with the arrival at the manor house of Charles Wall, who demolished most of the surviving cottages around the old church.[1] The name of the new occupant of the mill was A Hogg, whose trade is unknown but there are no records to suggest that he was a papermaker.[2]

Wall was succeeded in 1819 by the wealthy banker Henry Drummond. He rehoused the remaining villagers about a mile down the valley in Weston Street, which took over the name of Albury from the deserted village in the Park. Drummond was one of the twelve apostles of the Catholic Apostolic Church and Albury became its spiritual centre. In 1840 he built a church for the sect in the Park. He also closed the old parish church near the manor house and had a new church, said to have been mistakenly constructed of brick rather than stone, built in the new Albury. He then employed Pugin, who had recently designed the interiors of the Houses of Parliament, to rebuild the manor as a neo-Tudor mansion with, for example, 63 ornate brick chimneys, each one copied from a different source. The same style was used for houses in the new Albury and the former paper mill became a neo-Tudor laundry, with water-powered equipment, for the use of Albury Park mansion.

Henry Drummond's daughter married the son of the Duke of Northumberland and consequently the Albury estate later passed to the Duchy, which continues to own it. In 1969 the mansion house was purchased by Mutual Households Association Limited, an organisation which converts historic houses into apartments for retired people. It now has about fifty residents. However the extensive parkland and woods around the house, including the remains of the Evelyn gardens and the paper mill site, and much other local property, remain in the ownership of the Albury Estates. The old church can be visited and the Pugin laundry, converted into a residence, is visible from the car-parking area, but permission has to be obtained to enter the gardens.[3]

When the Unwins purchased Chilworth paper mill in 1870 and converted it to a printing works they transferred some of their work force from London and settled in the mill house themselves. From 1872 to 1884 the *Paper Mills Directory*, which from its first issue in 1860 provides much information on paper mills countrywide, was printed by the Unwins at Chilworth. After the disastrous fire of Saturday 26 November 1895, Unwins did not rebuild at Chilworth as the Duke of Northumberland, who owned the manor, would not allow them to extend the works and build cottages for their employees. They therefore searched for a new site and discovered another paper mill which had recently closed at Old Woking. They called their new premises 'The Saint Martha Printing Works' and their successors remain there to this day.[4]

Meanwhile the rubble at Chilworth was cleared and the site of the mill became part of the garden of the old mill house which had escaped the fire. All remains of the former Little Paper Mill have also disappeared but its drying house survives as a pair of cottages. At the end of the nineteenth century a turbine-operated pumping station was installed towards the south end of the paper mill dam to supply water to a reservoir just below Saint Martha's church. The water is now pumped by electricity and the turbines are unused. Upstream is the large, recently-created fish pond which drains through the seventeenth-century culvert under the small mill pond. The water still drops 14 feet (4.3m) into the channels which once housed waterwheels. Only one piece of machinery from Chilworth paper mill is known to have survived, an iron drying cylinder, 5 feet wide and 3 feet in diameter, from the paper-making machine. This was converted into a heavy roller for use by the neighbouring Blackheath Cricket Club as shown in figure 62.

In 1880, following the failure of Pavy Pretto & Co, the manufacturers of felted furniture fabric at Postford Mill, George Adams, who had held the lease for ten years, appealed to the Duke of Northumberland to allow him to give it up. The rent was £244 2s 0d, which seems high compared with the £40 paid by Unwins for Chilworth Mills, and even the £300 paid by Samuel Sharp for the extensive Chilworth Gunpowder Works. The Postford buildings were then used as a flock mill, tearing up woollen rags to produce stuffing for mattresses and furniture, but they were destroyed by fire in 1886.[5] Flock mills were particularly vulnerable to fire and this fate was also to befall one at Eashing which occupied a former paper mill.[6]

In 1909 the site of the original Postford Lower Mill was taken over by the Botting family who were previously corn millers at modern Albury. They therefore called their new premises Albury Mill and installed new roller-milling machinery rather than traditional mill-stones. The mill and much of this equipment survived until 1990, producing flour, which was used by local bakers for 'Albury' loaves, and animal feed. They also produced feed for trout which were farmed next to the corn mill on the site of the Magnay

Figure 62 Heavy roller at the Blackheath Cricket Club ground, made from a drying cylinder of a papermaking machine. The machine was last used at Chilworth paper mill in 1870. The roller is a prized possession of the Club but has been superseded by a heavier motorised one. Photo by Alan Crocker, 1983.

paper mill of the 1830s. The old waterwheel of this mill had been replaced by a water turbine in 1910. Bottings' Mill was demolished in the 1990s and the area was redeveloped for offices and the Mill Reach residential estate.[7]

The site of Postford Upper Mill, at Waterloo Pond, went permanently out of industrial use when it was closed by the Magnays. Their new 'upper mill' still stands in the grounds of Postford House. It probably remained unused for a time after the paper mill closed but a water turbine, which still survives, was installed in the 1920s when the building became a sawmill.[8]

The Gunpowder Works

The Duke of Northumberland sold the Chilworth estate in 1922. Local residents recall that an area near the tramway swing bridge was purchased by a Mr Roach who built some timber houses there. Many of the buildings of the gunpowder and cordite works were also used as dwellings and it is said that about twenty families lived on the site. The women's mess room of the Admiralty works was moved to Peaslake where, as 'the Hut' it was used as the village cinema and dance hall. It was later converted into cottages which were demolished in the 1990s. Conditions on the Chilworth site had deteriorated by the 1950s and the families living there were rehoused by the Council. Many of the buildings were demolished and cleared by about 1963. Other areas of the site are privately owned but served in part by way-marked public footpaths. From west to east, a public footpath from East Shalford reaches the site of the stamp mills of the seventeenth-century Lower Works, of which no visible traces remain. Between here and Blacksmith Lane, several buildings are still used for industrial purposes, including the manufacture of garden sheds. The central portion of the site, between Blacksmith Lane and the lane from Lockner Farm to Chilworth Manor, is owned by Guildford Borough Council which has erected information boards. Many ruined structures, including remains of 1860s and 1880s incorporating mills and twenty or more edge-runner mill stones, can be seen in this area. From the Lockner Farm lane, which is part of the Downs Link long-distance path, a public footpath continues eastwards on private land, through the site of the Admiralty cordite works to Postford and beyond.

Because of its historic importance the central area of the gunpowder works was granted protection as a Scheduled Ancient Monument in 1982 and in 1999 the scheduled area was extended to include part of the former smokeless powder works.[9]

*   *   *

Research on the history of the industries of the Tillingbourne is continuing and further recording of their remains is planned. The authors of this book would welcome information on any aspect of these industries and would like to appeal for any photographs or other memorabilia to be brought to light for the benefit of the community.

Notes

1. Walmsley, R C, *Albury Park* (Albury, 1974).
2. SHC, Land tax records (QS6/7, Albury).
3. Walmsley, see ref.1.
4. Unwin, P, *The Printing Unwins* (Allen & Unwin, 1976), 35–6, 38, 40, 49.
5. NEO, Alnwick, Letter of 12 May 1886 from Andrew Peebles; *Paper Mills Directory.*
6. Janaway, J, *Yesterday's Town: Godalming* (Barracuda, 1987), 55.
7. Members of SIHG video-recorded the roller-milling equipment in operation before the mill closed.
8. Crocker, A, 'Surrey Water Turbines' (to be published).
9. Crocker, G, *A Guide to the Chilworth Gunpowder Mills* (3rd edn, SIHG, 1999).

Glossary

alum: introduced into the Hollander or beating engine to fix dyes when making coloured paper; also used to fix size

asp: prop on the bridge across a vat against which the coucher rests a mould supporting a sheet of draining paper

beater or beating engine (papermaking): see *Hollander*

bedstone: the horizontal base on which edge runners turn

black powder: term used for old-fashioned gunpowder after the introduction of smokeless powder as a propellant for guns

bleaching: removal of colour from disintegrated rags by exposure to the sun, chlorine gas or chloride of lime

boiler: in papermaking, a container for boiling rags, esparto grass and other raw materials under pressure in a caustic soda solution

boiling house: in gunpowder mills, part of saltpetre refinery

breaker: a machine in which rags are broken down into individual fibres, bleached and washed to produce half-stuff for making paper

breaking down: reducing the size of lumps of gunpowder mill cake before pressing

breast-shot: waterwheel which water enters between '2 o'clock' and '4 o'clock'

brimstone: old term for sulphur

brown powder: see *cocoa powder*

calenders: chilled iron cylinders of paper-making machine which give the paper a smooth, glossy or other special finish

charcoal cylinders: retorts in which wood is distilled to produce a pure form of charcoal for use as an ingredient of gunpowder, introduced in the 1790s

charge: in gunpowder, the material being processed; termed a 'green charge' when it is unworked

china clay: filler which makes paper whiter, heavier and better able to take printing ink

clasp-armed: waterwheel with spokes forming a square around the shaft on which it is mounted

coal: old term for charcoal, as distinct from pit or 'sea' coal

cocoa powder: brown gunpowder made with incompletely carbonised wood or straw in place of charcoal

compass-armed: waterwheel with spokes radiating from the shaft on which it is mounted

composition house: building in which the ingredients of gunpowder were assembled; probably equivalent to a mixing house

cooperage: place where barrels are made

coppers: copper vessels for boiling

cordite: a smokeless propellant made from nitrocellulose and nitroglycerine *coucher:* workman in a hand-made paper mill who takes the mould with its sheet of wet paper from the vatman, inverts it in order to place the paper on a piece of felted wool fabric and repeats the process to produce a pile or post of usually 144 sheets

corning: granulating gunpowder, by forcing it through sieves in a shaking frame or later by passing it between toothed gunmetal or zinc rollers

countermark: watermark in paper containing the name or initials of the paper-maker, the date, and occasionally the name of the mill or county of manufacture

crown wheel: a gear wheel mounted near the top of the main vertical shaft of a watermill

cut: artificially dug water channel

cutter: equipment which cuts machine-made paper into individual sheets

cylinder house: see *charcoal cylinders*

dandy roll: wire roll of Fourdrinier machine which helps to form the paper; also produces markings which simulate the characteristic laid or wove markings of hand-made paper. Watermarking devices can also be attached to the roll.

deckle: loose frame of wood which the vatman places around his mould to limit the size of the sheet of paper he is making and which he removes before passing the mould to the coucher; alternatively the straps which restrict the width of paper made on a machine

deckle-edge: irregular thin edge of a sheet or roll of paper produced by a small amount of pulp seeping between the mould or endless web and the deckle

devil: in papermaking, machine for tearing rags and removing dust and dirt *drying cylinders:* heated, highly-polished, rotating metal cylinders of papermaking machine against which the paper is pressed by felts

drying house: building or loft with opening shutters in which individual sheets of paper are hung on cow-hair ropes to dry

dusting house: in gunpowder mills, a building in which dust is removed from gunpowder by gently tumbling it in a reel covered with sieve cloth; in papermaking, a building, sometimes part of the rag house, in which dust is removed from rags

edge runners: millstones (later iron runners) which roll around on their circumference on a circular bedstone

engine (papermaking): see *Hollander*

engine-sized paper: paper made from pulp containing size introduced in the beating engine

esparto: grass about 1 metre in height with large flat grey-green leaves which grows in North Africa and Spain; used from about 1860 as a raw material for high quality paper

excise duty: in the paper industry, tax on paper introduced in 1712 and finally repealed in 1861. Excise numbers were allocated to mills between 1816 and 1851.

expense magazine: place to store gunpowder temporarily between stages of manufacture

felts: pieces of felted woollen fabric, which absorb water from individual sheets of paper, or continuous felted blankets and rollers used for the same purpose with Fourdrinier machines

Fourdrinier: machine for making continuous rolls of paper first developed successfully by Bryan Donkin at Bermondsey in 1802–6, with finance from the London wholesale stationers Henry and Sealy Fourdrinier

frame: see *mould*

glazing: in gunpowder, applying a final polish to grains of powder by tumbling them in revolving barrels, with or without black lead; in papermaking, producing a smooth finish on sheets of paper by polishing with a stone, hammering, or pressing and shearing between metal plates; alternatively passing machine-made paper through calenders

gloom stove: old type of stove for drying gunpowder, heated by the back of an iron fireplace in an adjacent room

granulating: see *corning*

gudgeon: metal journal bearing in the end of a wooden shaft or axle

gunpowder: explosive made from saltpetre, charcoal and sulphur

half-stuff: in papermaking, coarse pulp with separated fibres, often bleached, produced in a Hollander or breaker

hog: stirring device which prevents the fibres of the stuff settling at the bottom of a papermaker's vat

Hollander: beating engine to produce pulp or stuff for papermaking, introduced into England from Holland in about 1700. It consists of a large tank in which rag fibres mixed with water are cut, pounded and frayed between a rotating roller and a bed-plate, which are fitted with blades or bars.

incorporating: intimately combining saltpetre, charcoal and sulphur to form gunpowder

laid paper: paper with characteristic straight-line markings of the closely spaced wires of a mould or dandy roll and the more widely spaced perpendicular chain markings (see also *wove*)

last: a measure of gunpowder containing 24 cwt

lattices: wire meshes over which rags for paper-making are cut against fixed vertical knives, the dust falling through into bins

layer: workman in a hand-made paper mill who places damp warm sheets of felt ready to receive sheets of paper from the coucher, presses the resulting post of paper and then separates the sheets of paper from the pieces of felt

leat: open watercourse carrying water to a mill etc

machine (papermaking): see *Fourdrinier*

magazine: building used to store explosives

mortars: in papermaking, water-laden troughs of a stamping-mill used for making pulp

mould: rectangular frame of wood supporting a bronze wire cover which the vat-man dips into the vat to form a sheet of paper (see *laid* and *wove*)

mould-made: paper which is made on a machine with a cylindrical mould and which simulates the quality and properties of hand-made paper

mill: industrial establishment, process unit or individual machine, depending on the context

mill cake: the product of a gunpowder incorporating mill

mixing: in gunpowder, combining the weighed ingredients prior to incorporating

overshot: waterwheel which water enters just over the top

pestle mill: pestles and mortars operated by gearing from a power source; also known as stamp or trough mill

post: stack of 144 sheets of paper interleaved with felts

press: machine, operated hydraulically or by hand with a screw. A gunpowder press is used to compress mill cake into hard slabs prior to corning; in papermaking a wet press is used for squeezing water from newly formed wet sheets of paper and a dry press for flattening sheets of dry paper.

press cake: hard slabs of compressed gunpowder

propellant: an explosive that fires projectiles from a gun

pulp: see *stuff*

rag house: building in which rags for paper-making are dusted, cut to remove seams, and sorted into qualities. Typically these are: superfine; fine; stitches of fine; middling; seams and stitches of middling; coarse; the very coarse being rejected for white paper but used for brown paper.

reel: roller at the end of a paper-making machine on which finished paper is wound; in a gunpowder mill, a cylinder covered with sieve cloth, often sloping, for removing dust from grains of gunpowder

salle (pronounced sol): finishing room where paper is inspected, polished, sorted into sizes and qualities, and packed

saltpetre: potassium nitrate

saltpetre earth: nitrogenous earth collected and maintained by gunpowder makers as a source of saltpetre

sea coal: pit coal for fuel, brought to London by sea from north-east England

separating: in gunpowder mills, separating grains of gunpowder from dust

shaking frame: frame on which sieves are mounted, kept in motion by a crank from a power source

sizing house: building or room in which a workman, known as a sizer, passes sheets of pressed paper through a bath of warm size to make them less absorbent *smokeless powder:* term used in the late nineteeenth century for propellants made by the new technology of the time, eg cordite

sol: see *salle*

stampers: water-powered iron-tipped hammers by which rags are macerated to produce pulp for papermaking

stamp mill: see *pestle mill*

standers: see *tribles*

stove: heated building for drying gunpowder by setting it out in canvas-lined trays on shelving, heated by a fireplace (see *gloom stove*) or later by piped steam

stuff: fine pulp or pap ready for making paper which is stored and mixed in a stuff chest before being transferred to a vat

swimming wheel: eighteenth century millwrighting term for a large horizontal gear wheel which engages with smaller gear wheels to drive machinery in a watermill

traverse: a high bank forming a protective screen between a gunpowder danger building and its surroundings

tribles: horizontal frames supporting lines of waxed-hair rope over which sheets of paper are hung for drying. When full of paper a trible is lifted in the drying loft to rest on pegs in vertical posts called standers.

trough: launder carrying water from a mill pond to the top of a waterwheel; beam housing the mortars of a pestle, stamp or trough mill for incorporating gunpowder

trough mill: see *pestle mill*

tub-sized paper: paper which is sized, after being pressed and dried, by passing sheets through a bath of warm size

vat: a large open tank containing warm pulp into which the vatman dips his mould to make a sheet of hand-made paper or from which pulp flows on the endless web of a papermaking machine

vatman: skilled workman in a hand-made paper mill who forms a sheet of wet paper by dipping his mould into the pulp in the vat and then shaking it to remove surplus water and cause the fibres to intertwine

watch house: building on a gunpowder works, at a safe distance from danger buildings, where workmen were based during working hours

watermark: mark on paper arising from a wire design, typically Britannia, a Crown, the Royal Arms, a Fleur-de-Lis, a Lion, 'Pro Patria' or a Horn, sewn with fine wire on the mould or dandy roll. 'Shadow' watermarks, such as the portraits in modern banknote papers, are produced by shaping the wove wire.

wheel-pit: recess to accommodate a waterwheel

whited-brown paper: cream coloured paper used for packing

wood pulp: inexpensive mechanical pulp made by grinding timber or better quality chemical pulp produced by cooking timber in caustic soda, sulphate of soda and bi-sulphite of lime

wove paper: paper with ill-defined markings of the woven fine wires of a mould or dandy roll (see also *laid*)

INDEX

cf: cordite factory; gp: gunpowder; mf: manufacturer; pm: papermaker; wk: worker; illustrations in italic.